CHRIS PEARSON
M0JRQ
SUMMER 2007

THE G-QRP CLUB ANTENNA HANBOOK
Second Edition
2007

Published by BearFace for the
G-QRP Club

ISBN 978-0-9549302-1-9

Distributed by
G-QRP Club Sales, Graham Firth, G3MFJ,
13, Wynmore Drive, Bramhope, Leeds LS16 9DQ
g3mfj@gqrp.co.uk

THE G-QRP CLUB
ANTENNA HANDBOOK

CHRIS PEARSON
M0JRQ
SUMMER 2007

A glance at the cumulative SPRAT index confirms our interest in antennas: With a LOW POWER S.W.R. INDICATOR in SPRAT's first issue, it began in earnest with an item in issue two, IMPROVING THE EFFICIENCY OF SHORT L.F. BAND AERIALS by Angus Taylor, G8PG and has continued right up to Spring 2007. In that time there have been almost 200 titles under the heading Antenna and half as many again categorized as ATUs and Accessories.

And if any one member and contributor to SPRAT has been an inspiration and a constant companion to the antenna experimenter, it has been Gus. Retiring as writer of SPRAT's essential Antennas-Anecdotes-Awards column in Spring 2007, our thanks go out to Gus along with a promise that we shall continue to tradition he has done so much to establish.

The number of antenna-related items appearing in SPRAT has at least doubled since the first edition of the G-QRP Club Antenna Handbook was published back in 1992. Since then the G-QRP Yahoo! Group has also flourished, becoming a lively and prolific forum for the exchange of opinion and expertise on antennas.

So it has been a massive undertaking - not to mention a joy - to read all that material, categorize it and to select the items you will find in this second edition of the G-QRP Club Antenna Handbook. The urge to make

CHRIS PEARSON
M0JRQ
JULY 2007

them, try them, compare them has, in many instances, been a genuine threat to ever finishing this book!

I have attempted to mix items that describe complete antenna projects with others that report on experiments and discuss ideas that may lead on to projects of your own.

I'd like to thank everyone who has helped in the creation of this handbook and, most especially, the contributors to SPRAT. Those contributors don't just ensure that we all look forward to SPRAT every quarter; they have written the material that made compiling this book possible.

Chris Pearson
M0JRQ
G-QRP 11904

To the memory of old Bill
and to the achievement and passion of the pioneers
of amateur radio

TEN THOUGHTS ABOUT ANTENNAS

1. It is the current that does the work. Always try and get the high current portion of an antenna as far above ground as possible, and avoid bending it.

2. A coaxial fed half wave dipole should always be carefully resonated with the aid of a dip meter. An end fed half wave, on the other hand, should be made a metre or so longer or shorter than the resonant length, as this provides an easier feed point impedance.

3. At DX the signal from an antenna 20m high will normally be at least 6dB up on an antenna 10m high. (This should be compulsory learning for all planning officers and XYLs !!!)

4. If you want to get the maximum amount of wire into a given area try a loop.

5. A doublet will only be truly balanced if each half is individually trimmed to the required frequency.

6. This also applies to the groundplane. Connect each radial individually to the top and resonate the system, then connect all four to the top.

7. If you want to get the current in a vertical as far above ground as possible, use a T antenna fed at the bottom via an ATU.

8. A simple end-fed, multi-band antenna which requires no ground connection and matches easily is the W3EDP (84ft with a 17 ft cps.)

9. If you find any antenna giving "rf in the shack" on a particular band, cut a quarter wave counterpoise wire for that band, and connect it to the ground terminal on your rig or atu.

10. Be proud of owning and knowing how to use a good atu such as a Z-match. This will allow you to load a whole range of antennas with maximum ease.

GUS TAYLOR
G8PG
SPRAT 86
SPRING 1996

G-QRP CLUB ANTENNA HANDBOOK

CONTENTS

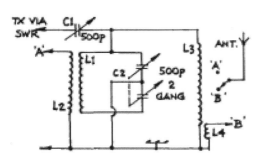

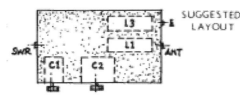

SUGGESTED LAYOUT

VC1   One section of a 500pF broadcast type

VC2   Both gangs of a 500pF broadcast type

L1   6 turns PVC stranded wire on 2½ inch diameter water piping

L2   As L1 with turns wound on side by side with L1 on same former.
      Coils mounted away from the side of the box

L3   13 turns as L1

L4   6 turns wound as L2 at earthy end of L3

S1   SPDT toggle (position A tunes 14, 21 and 28MHz, probably the new
      bands but not tried. Position B tunes 3.5 and 7MHz).

The unit is wired as shown for coaxial fed antennas. For a
balanced feed, disconnect the bottom of L2 and L4 from earth
and connect to a separate terminal or socket.

Used with a full size G5RV, a perfect match on all bands,
without plug-in coils, is obtained. A direct comparison with
a commercial tuner costing 20 times the cost of this design,
showed no difference in performance. A standard toggle
switch is used for S1.

To make a compact unit, a built in SWR indicator could be
employed, but was not considered as my Argonaut has a SWR
indicator incorporated in it.

**FRANK LEE
G3YZZ
SPRAT 38
SPRING 1984**

SIMPLE LED SWR BRIDGE

Inspired by G4TKV's comments about Superbright LEDs, see RadCom (TT May 1997), I modified the popular QRP SWR Bridge by replacing the micrometer with a superbright LED. Unlike ordinary LEDs, the Superbright will glow with a current of less than 10 micro-amps.

With less than 1 watt output from the TX, the LED is fully illuminated and extinguishes as the load is matched for minimum VSWR. Easy to use and it takes up little panel space – ideal for that miniature QRP rig.

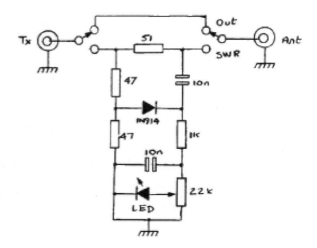

JOHN YOUNG
G0WQR
SPRAT 93
WINTER 1997/8

A BATTERY AND SWR INDICATOR WITH DUO-LED

In order to monitor and to tune the aerial when operating portable, I wanted to build some sort of SWR indicator into my little rig. Although there was enough space inside the rig for the pickup circuit, I didn't find a suitable place on the front panel for a meter and a potentiometer. So I began to experiment with a Duo-LED as a substitute and came out with the circuit shown.

A Duo-LED consists of a green and a red LED integrated into a single case and as the LEDs are close together, the two colours mix almost perfectly. This property is used in the SWR Indicator to provide a change of colour from red via yellow to green while the ATU is tuned, whereas the intensity of the light represents the applied power.

For simplicity I used the pickup circuit of G4ZNQ (described in SPRAT No. 61), which needs only few components and no adjustments at all. The choice of the cores seems to be not very critical with this application, as no absolute readings are required. Of course any other form of an SWR bridge could be used instead.

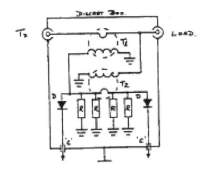

See *A Bi-directional Inline Wattmeter* by David Stockton G4ZNQ SPRAT 61 Winter 1989/90

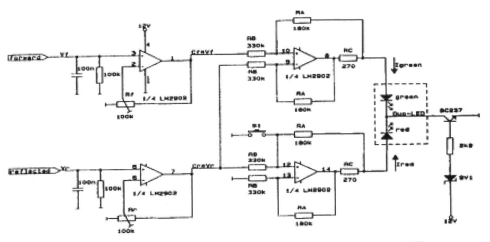

$$Igreen = (Crevf - Crevr) \cdot Ra / Rb \cdot Rc$$
$$Ired = Crevr \cdot Ra / Rb \cdot Rc$$

MATTHIAS VOLKERT
DF4SQ
SPRAT 63
SUMMER 1990

The forward and reflected voltages are amplified by the first two opamps of an LM2902 (OR LM324) package. The gain is set by Rf and Rr. The remaining two devices form a voltage controlled current source for each LED. The current through the red LED is directly proportional to the reflected voltage. The current through the green LED is a function of forward voltage minus reflected voltage (see equations at the bottom of the circuit diagram). As the total current through both LEDs is determined only by the forward voltage, brightness and colour are independent functions of applied power and SWR.

By means of S1 the red LED can be turned off to check whether a perfect match is already reached.

The LEDs are connected to ground via a transistor. Due to the zener diode the LEDs are switched off when the supply voltage falls below about 10 Volts thus providing additionally a simple way to monitor the battery.

For alignment apply as much power into a 50 Ohms resistor (SWR=1) as you want for maximum brightness and adjust Rf for 10 Volts at the amplifier output pin 1. This is equivalent to a current of 20mA through the green LED. Then change the load into a 150 Ohms resistor (SWR=3) and adjust Rr for 10 Volts at Pin 7, so that the whole current will flow through the red LED. This upper limit may of course also be set to another SWR value if preferred.

BALANCED FEEDER MOD FOR T-MATCH ATUS

**T SORBIE
GM3MXN
SPRAT 103
SUMMER 2000**

When modifying a T-Match ATU (such as the MFJ ATU) for balanced feeder, the use of a 4 to 1 balun on the output side is bad practice and can lead to losses, it is much better to place the balun on the input side, and if it is a choke balun it will make the ATU balanced, if not grounded, I know that the purists will say a wood or plastic box should be used , but in practice I have found that the balance is good.

I have a 1 to 1 choke balun on the input side made by winding 20 turns RG58U coax on each of 2 ferrite rods in series, and on the output side I use the coax socket to feed the balanced output. The only drawback is a slight hand capacity but I can tune every band including 50 MHz and don't use QRO as you could get an RF burn from the case, no trouble with QRP. No earth should be connected, unless coax feeder is used.

Through the years, aerials and antenna-tuners have been food for thoughts in the world of Amateur Radio. The Dutch gang on 80 spent many hours discussing these subjects and in "The Dutch Pub" on 3.777 MHz they still appear to be popular items. Many seem to prefer the use of a doublet combined with a Z-match.

In a tuner that is commonly known as a "Z-match" the open feeders of a doublet are coupled with a tuned circuit. In fact, there are two of these circuits. One for a "higher" frequency range and one for a "lower" (fig.1). The coils are supposed not to be "seen" by frequencies for which they are not used as they either work as a short circuit or as a choke. The "split stator" variable capacitor either resonates with one coil as a pair of variable capacitors switched parallel or with the other as a pair in series.

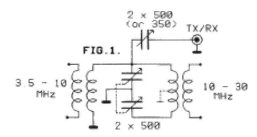

A first modification was made by Louis Varney, G5RV, who called the output circuit via a capacitor to the hot end of the resonating coil a matter of "bad engineering" (ref. 1). OM Varney suggested to make taps on relatively cold ends of the coils, either near the hard ground of one coil or near the virtual ground of the other (fig.2).

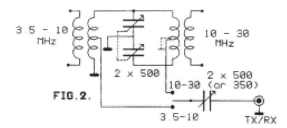

Personally I do not really enjoy the winding of coils. For HF I consider them to be large lump things that are a chore to make. When related to a "standard" Z-match, this feeling is enhanced by the fact that I don't like the idea of coils that are not "seen" by certain frequencies. Though used as such by many hams I think the coils are too much alike to use this principle. So I restricted myself to one tuned circuit and a 2 x 500 pF split stator. The DPDT switch gives the tuned coil a hard ground and switches the two sections of the split stator parallel for the frequency range between 3.5 and 10 MHz. For the frequency range from 10 to 30 MHz the sections of the split stator are in series and the tuned coil has a virtual ground. Use a dipmeter to check whether the whole range from 3.5 to 30Mhz can be tuned. Using a 32mm PVC tube as a former, I needed 10 close wound windings of thick insulated single core electricity wire for the tuned circuit and 8 windings of similar wire with the insulation removed wound around the first coil for coupling.

ROBERT VAN DER ZAAL
PA3BHK
SPRAT 86
SPRING 1996

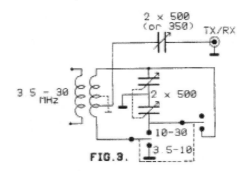

FIG.3.

The coil is tapped at 3 windings from the hard ground for 3.5 to 10 MHz which means 2 windings from the virtual ground when used between 10 and 30 MHz. This way we only need one pair of coils and have a more appropriate output circuit.

Now we are left with one burning question: DOES IT WORK? The answer is quite diplomatically: usually it does. But the range in which a Z-match can actually match the complex impedance of an aerial and its feeders to the usually required 50 Ohms is limited. My doublet that is based on a G5RV dipole causes no problems and can be matched quite easily with an SWR better than 1.5 on all bands including the WARC bands. But my "small" horizontal V- dipole (2x4 m) for the "DX - bands causes difficulties on 14 and 28 MHz. One way to match it on these two bands is by changing the length of the feeders until the tuner works. It is a good thing that these days we have chocolate blocks and slotted ribbon feeders!

Some experimenting resulted in a jack of all trades and a master in many. The tuner can be build in a small box which seems ideal for portable QRP experiments. However, it might cause difficulties with some aerial systems. If your aerial system gets along with this Z-match, you will find it a handy tuner with only two controls and a switch. In the high range tuning becomes quite sharp so the use of a reduction drive is recommended. Who continues experimenting with this popular tuner? I look forward to reading about it in future issues of SPRAT

Reference:
1 John D Heys, G3BDQ: Practical Wire Antennas, 1989
   RSGB, London, UK

NO-COST FIELD STRENGTH METER

I discovered this idea by accident.
Using a multimeter on the AC ranges - grounding the negative lead and raising the positive as an antenna makes a simple FS Meter.
It may be a useful idea to SPRAT readers.

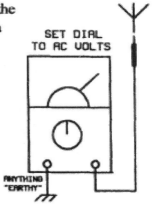

JOHN GARDNER
GW4KVJ
SPRAT 103
SUMMER 2000

In spite of what some advertisers may tell you, most of the normal antenna adjustments that amateurs need to make can be carried out by simply using a good SWR Meter. However there are times when more information is needed, such as knowing the impedance at the shack end of the coax feeder. The current vogue instrument for solving such problems is the antenna analyser. The MAA does the job of a commercial analyser but costs a lot less.

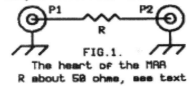

FIG.1.
The heart of the MAA
R about 50 ohms, see text

Your first reaction may well be "you must be kidding". However keep the faith and read on. Yes you do need some more equipment but this is only gear that any normal amateur can be expected to have or to be prepared to make. The extra bits are, a low power (1-2 watt) transmitter for the bands of interest and a RF voltmeter. The first can be provided by turning the wick down on your transceiver. An RF voltmeter is easily made, see figure 2.

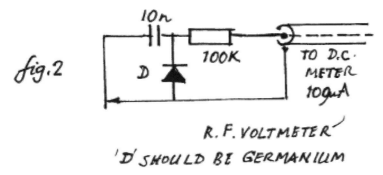

R.F. VOLTMETER
'D' SHOULD BE GERMANIUM

How to use the MAA

To use the MAA you don't need to know how it works but, for those who want to know the theory is covered at the end of this article.

Connect the RF source to P1 and the load whose impedance you wish to measure to P2. connect the RF voltmeter between P1 and ground and set the RF source to give about 7 volts across P1 (Vi). Now measure the voltage across the resistor (Vs) and the voltage from P2 to ground (Vz).

For purposes of explanation let us assume: Vi = 7 volts, Vs = 4 volts, and Vz = 5 volts, also R = 47 ohms. Now refer to figure 3 [not actual size], draw a line OA about 10" long, mark S so that OS = 4". Place a compass point at O and swing an arc of length 7". Place a compass point at S and swing an arc of length 5". Call the intersection of the arcs P. We now have OP = 7" and SP = 5" Drop a perpendicular to OA at X and measure SX = 1.05" and PX = 4.85"

I have chosen to make 1" equivalent to 1 volt, however any unit of length may be used.

GERALD STANCEY
G3MCK
SPRAT 103
SUMMER 2000

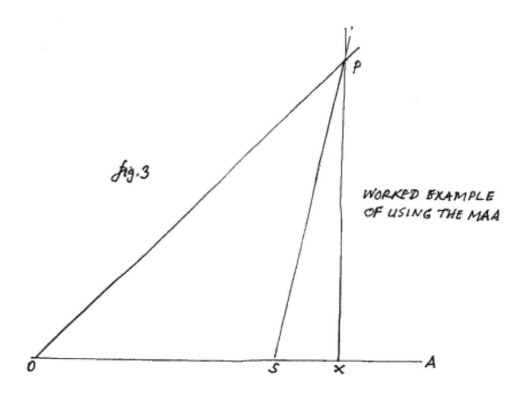

fig.3

WORKED EXAMPLE OF USING THE MAA

The impedance across P2 is calculated as follows:
Resistive component = 1.05 x 47 / 4.00 = 12.3 ohms
Reactive component = 4.85 x 47 / 4.00 = 60.0 ohms

To find the nature of the reactance, i.e. is it inductive or capacitive place an inductor of about 60 ohms reactance in series with the unknown impedance at P2 and re-measure Vi, Vs, and Vz. If Vz ≈ Vi + Vs then the component has capacitive reactance, otherwise it is inductive. Instead of using an inductor you can use a capacitor of about 60 ohms reactance and invert the above logic.

Special cases

If Vz = Vi + Vs, then the load is a pure resistance.

If $Vz^2 = Vi^2 + Vs^2$ then the load is a pure reactance.

Hence this technique can be used for measuring reactances. For example, by suitable choice of frequency, capacitors in the range of 20 pF to 2000 pF can be measured.

If a quarter wave stub, with the far end open circuit, is connected to P2, then $Vz = 0$. this can be used for making stubs or for finding the velocity factor of coax. For best results it is advisable to make a unit specially for this purpose with the diode probe built directly actoss P2.

Construction details

The basic unit can be built on a piece of PCB. The value of R is not critical, say 33 - 68 ohms and 1W rating. It must be non-inductive and it is OK to use parallel combinations such as 2 x 100 ohms to get the required resistance and wattage. The actual value you use for r must be substituted in the worked example for 47.

I have found that a normal 100 micro amp analogue meter is best to use with the RF probe as non-analogue meters can be susceptible to RF pick up. Calibrate the probe to allow for the diode off-set as follows.

Put a resistor of about the same value as R across P2 and measure the three voltages as before. The diode offset (D) is given by:

$$D = Vi - Vs - Vz$$

This value must be added to each of the three readings before using them to construct the voltage diagram. In other words if $D = 0.3$ then in the above example Vi was actually measured as 6.7 volts.

Low power RF source

If your transceiver cannot be adjusted to give about 1 - 2 watts or if you feel unhappy about connecting it to an unknown impedance then feed the MAA through an attenuator. Anything over 6 dB will virtually ensure that the rig sees a suitable load. Don't forget to make the attenuator with resistors that can dissipate the excess power.

Pros and cons

This is a practical rather than a precision instrument. However it will put you in the right ball park and enable you to proceed by the usual amateur methods of cut and try. Incidentally the professionals solve their problems this way but call it sorting out teething troubles!

Compared with commercial equipment the MAA takes a little more effort to use. In practice it can only be used in the amateur bands and probably in the shack. In its favour is not only its low cost but the deeper understanding you need to use it. To put it bluntly if Impedance is a closed book to you why are you bothering to measure it?

The theory bit

You don't need to read this to use the MAA but it is only applied RAE theory.

Consider a resistance in series with an inductance, see figure 4. Apply an AC voltage across the combination and measure the three voltages, Vz, Vr, and V1. You will find that they are related by the formula $Vz^2 = Vr^2 + V1^2$

This relationship can be represented by a right angled triangle whose sides are in proportion to Vz, Vr and V1.

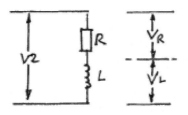

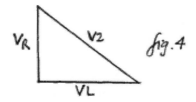

Now put a resistor Rs in series with the combinations and apply an AC voltage across them such that Vz remains unchanged. We can now draw the voltage of figure 4 to give figure 5. You will see that this is the one we drew when we used the MAA for measuring an Impedance. In other words the MAA has effectively given us a way of getting inside the unknown impedance to measure Vr and V1.

Now who was it who was saying that the RAE is of no real use to amateurs?

VOLTAGE RELATIONSHIPS
IN A CIRCUIT WITH
RESISTANCE & REACTANCE

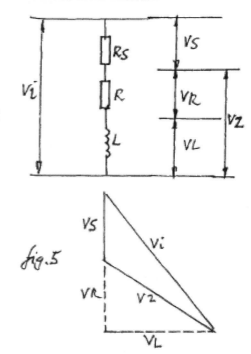

fig.5

VOLTAGE RELATIONSHIPS IN THE MAA

Background

Electric lamps have a long history of use as rf indicators in amateur radio. Indeed prior to World War 2 they were universal as rf sniffers, for indicators in absorption wavemeters, and as tuning indicators for setting up certain types of antennas.
Figs 1 to 6 show a number of these uses, which will now be described in greater detail.
Figure 1,

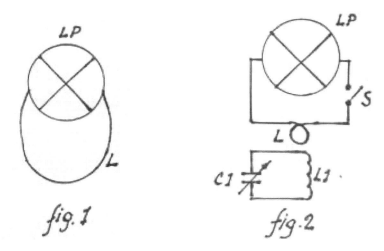

fig. 1

fig. 2

This shows a typical "rf sniffer" circuit . By coupling the single turn coil L to tuned circuits in a TX or an ATU it is possible to (a) prove whether or not there is rf present in the circuit under test and then (b) tune it for maxim rf output, simply by monitoring how brightly the lamp glows. In a practical circuit the lamp holder can be mounted on a wood or plastic handle for ease of use.

Figure 2.

In this application the lamp and coil are mounted so that they are permanently coupled to (say) the PA or ATU output circuit to allow it to be tuned for maximum output. Switch S allows the circuit to be disabled once tuning is completed.

GUS TAYLOR
G8PG
SPRAT 117
WINTER 2003/4

Figure 3

In this application the lamp acts as the indicator in an absorption wavemeter, resonance being indicated by maximum lamp glow. If required coil L can be tapped and switched to provide several frequency ranges.

Figure 4.

Way back in 1937 newly licenced 17 year old G8PG managed to save up enough money to buy a cheap hot wire rf ammeter. Sadly, no one had told him how sensitive such meters are to rf power overload, and it was soon bunrned out!Fortunately the main antenna was a CURRENT FED type (W3EDP) so an ordinary 15 watt electric lamp was inserted at the base of the antenna, used to tune up, and shorted out when not in use, and much DX was worked. Note the words "CURRENT FED". It will not work at the base of a voltage fed antenna.

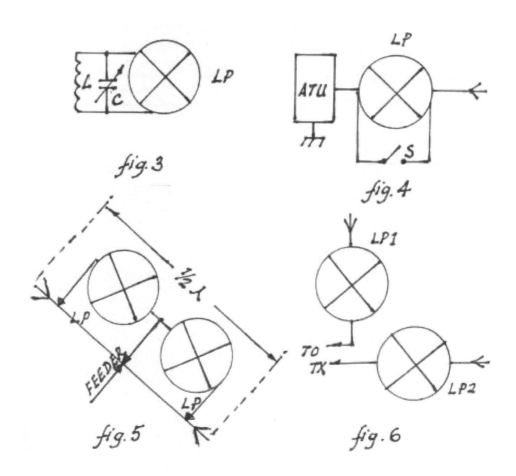

fig.3

fig.4

fig.5

fig.6

Figure 5.

This shows how two lamps are used to tune a Windom antenna for best performance. The theoretical point of feeder attchment is worked out from the antenna manual information and the feeder is attached. Two lamps are connected at equal distances from the feeder, the feeder is moved along the antenna until the two lamps glow equally brightly, the feeder is then permanently attached and the lamps are removed.

Figure 6.

This shows how two lamps are inserted one in each leg of an "up and outer" antenna to tune it for maximum performance. If both legs are high in the air this may not be necessary

but if the horizontal leg is close to ground it certainly is. The method is to cut the vertical leg to formula, do the same for the horizontal leg, insert the lamps, then trim the horizontal leg until its lamp glow is the same as that of the vertical leg. In tests by that Grand OM Rockey (W9SCH) he found that if the horizontal leg was 1m above ground it had to be shortened by over a meter to bring the two halves of the antenna into current balance. (This could be an important point when using counterpoise wires close to ground, as using the theoretical length may not give resonance.)

The circuit is shown in Figure 1. The 7 turn coil is of 26 SWG enamelled copper wire, tapped at the third turn and wound on a

THE LOOPSTICK RADIATION METER/ ABSORPTION WAVEMETER

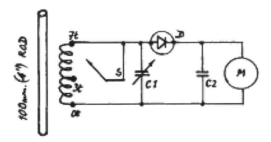

4 inch ferrite rod (loopstick) salvaged from a discarded b.c. receiver. C1 is 500p, C2 1000p, and D a germanium diode. The meter used was 0-200 uA, but with tight coupling to the rf source meters up to 0-1mA should work. IMPORTANT CONSTRUCTIONAL NOTE :- build the circuit in a plastic or wood case, as the signal pick-up is entirely via the ferrite rod. In our model the range with S1 closed was 28-10 MHz and with S1 open 10-3.5 MHz. Other ferrite rods may produce a slightly different result. For maximum coupling to the rf source point the end of the rod with the coil on it at the source. If the meter goes off scale increase the angle between the source and the rod. With the rod at ringhtangles to the source (say an antenna wire) the rf pickup is virtually zero. The meter can be calibrated with the aid of a dip meter, calibrated TX, or other calibrated rf source.

AAA TECHNICAL STAFF
SPRAT 85
WINTER 1995/6

THE PORTATEST

This simple instrument provides the QRP operator with an absorption wavemeter/radiation meter/voltmeter/continuity tester for /P and /M work.

With S2 in the RF position it is an absorption wavemeter and radiation meter. Positions V1 and V2 provide 0-15V and 0-300V measurements. The O position provides continuity tests. The device can be built in any box. If the coil is inside the box a short length of wire can be attached to A for RF pickup when laid near the aerial. If 1% tolerance resistors are used voltage readings will be accurate.

If coil L1 is adjusted to just cover 3.5MHz with C1 at max it should be possible to cover all bands 3.5 to 21MHz in the RF position by adjusting the tap so that with S1 closed, the 14 and 21MHz bands are covered.

If the O position is calibrated against known values of resistors and a calibration chart is made, resistance measurements may also be made. In this position VR1 is used for zero (FSD) setting.

Apart from use with the rig, this unit can save the /M op a few pounds if he has electrical faults on the road.

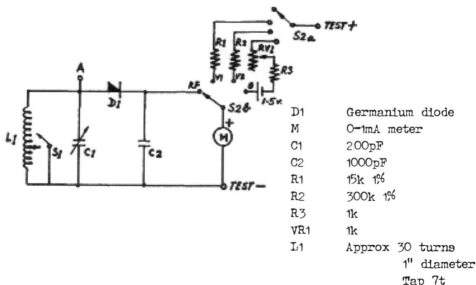

D1	Germanium diode
M	0-1mA meter
C1	200pF
C2	1000pF
R1	15k 1%
R2	300k 1%
R3	1k
VR1	1k
L1	Approx 30 turns 1" diameter Tap 7t

GUS TAYLOR
G8PG
SPRAT 12
DECEMBER 1977

This device adapts the GM4ZNX power meter for quiet tuning of the antenna. By this I mean reducing the power radiated during tune-up to less than a hundredth of its original value, while not reducing the sensitivity of the measurement. It also ensures that the transmitter has a good 50 ohms load during the tune-up process. It incorporates an idea from an article by Underhill and Lewis (Electronics Letters 4/1/79).

The heart of David's power meter is a dual directional coupler. It consists of just two transformers. It has a through line connecting the RF input to the RF output, and a coupled line, to which the diode detectors and the 50 ohm loads (two 100 ohm resistors in parallel) are connected. The power flowing in the coupled line depends on the turns-ratio of the transformers. For 12:1 turns ratio the coupled line has a hundredth and forty-fourth of the through line power (-21.58 dB).

The first diagram shows the conventional method of measuring reflected power used in an ATU adjustment. The transmitter and antenna are connected to the opposite ends of the through line. So the antenna is supplied with the full output of the transmitter. The antenna is assumed to reflect a proportion of the incident power and the detector measures 1/144th of the reflected power.

If the transmitter and the reflected power detector are interchanged (fig 2) then only 1/144th of the transmitter power arrives at the antenna. Since the antenna is still reflecting the same proportion of the incident power this is measured by the detector on the through line as the same power as in the previous case. The major difference is that only 1/144th of the previous power is radiated, and the major part of the transmitter power is dissipated in the 50 ohm load on the coupled line.

The modification to the GM4ZNX power meter consists of adding a switch to interchange the transmitter and one detector, and increasing the power rating of one of the 50 ohm load resistors to the full transmitter output power. The forward power meter will read the full transmitter power in the tune position, even though only a small proportion of this is being radiated. It used to read 1/144th of this power so an attenuator has been added to rectify the situation.

Although not strictly necessary, I have increased the power rating of the second reverse power sensing circuit to 5 watts in case the transmitter is inadvertently connected to the antenna jack.

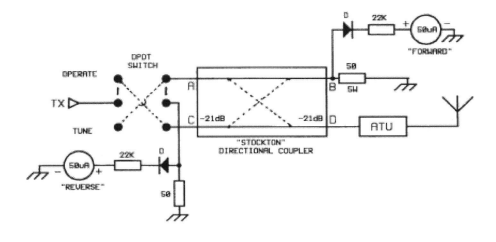

TONY LYMER
GM0DHD
SPRAT 97
WINTER 1998/9

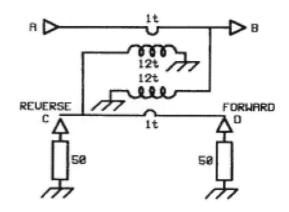

Just a couple of comments....

1) I checked the output in the tune position for generated harmonics of the carrier under matched and 2:1 VSWR conditions, but I didn't see any greater than -60 dB below the carrier output in the tune position. This shows that the diode in the reverse power detector doesn't generate harmonics, which might cause TVI while tuning.

2) The user has to tune for minimum reflected power, not maximum forward power. In fact, the forward power should remain fairly constant, because the match should not vary very much. (This may not be intuitive to some people.)

3) Just because the power has been reduced by ~20 dB while tuning up, this doesn't mean that the signal won't be heard. Interference to other stations will still occur, albeit at a reduced level. Normal courtesies (QRL?) still need to be used.

A UBIQUITOUS
L NETWORK

L can be 40 turns of 0.670 mm (22 swg) enamelled copper wire on a 2.5 cm former. Tap at 2 turns, 4 turns then every 4 turns. CV can be 150p or larger. With a 50 ohm TX input on SK1 and an antenna on T2 antenna impedances of greater than 50 ohms can be matched. With a 50 ohm TX output connected to SK2 and the antenna to T1 antenna impedances of lower than 50 ohms, such as those of whips or short lf band antennas can be matched to 50 ohms. If desired the taps can be wired to a suitable multi-position rotary switch . Note that if a metal cabinet is used L must be mounted at least its own diameter clear of any metal.

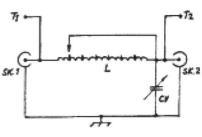

AAA TECHNICAL STAFF
SPRAT 91
SUMMER 1997

The ONER range of units is very well known, it all started with the transmitter from George Burt GM3OXX who gave the design to the G-QRP Club. This latest addition to the range is also on an (almost) one square inch PCB but for mounting purposes we have added two edges. If you wish to keep to the true ONER tradition you can cut off these edges of course.

A BI-DIRECTIONAL INLINE WATTMETER : SPRAT 61 by David Stockton GM4ZNX is one of the classics of QRP design. This unit is a miniature version of the Stockton wattmeter which is a full four port hybrid and is totally reversible. If a signal is passed through one connector and out of the other into some unknown load and both of the other connectors are connected to a fifty ohm load then the hybrid passes a fraction of the power passing forward through the unit to the other pair of connectors.

It is almost identical to the full Stockton Directional Wattmeter but in this case solely for QRP use. I.E. under 5 watt right up to 145MHz It has been tried with some success on 70Cms but the accuracy of our dummy load is questionable at this frequency.
It is bi-directional of course but in this application it uses just the one meter and a switch. Winding the cores is fairly easy providing you remember that once through the middle of the yellow core is one turn. Put 14 turns of the fine wire on the core and spread them evenly. Keep the wire tight, (it will be beneficial to use some bees wax or hot glue to hold the wire in place)

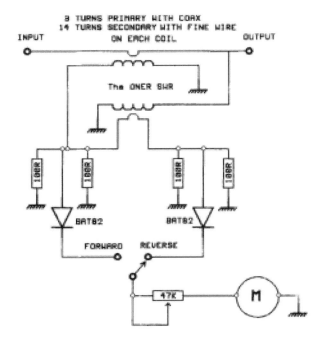

**DICK PASCOE
G0BPS
SPRAT 91
SUMMER 1997**

The ONER range of units is very well known, it all started with the transmitter from George Burt GM3OXX who gave the design to the G-QRP Club. This latest addition to the range is also on an (almost) one square inch PCB but for mounting purposes we have added two edges. If you wish to keep to the true ONER tradition you can cut off these edges of course.

A BI-DIRECTIONAL INLINE WATTMETER : SPRAT 61 by David Stockton GM4ZNX is one of the classics of QRP design. This unit is a miniature version of the Stockton wattmeter which is a full four port hybrid and is totally reversible. If a signal is passed through one connector and out of the other into some unknown load and both of the other connectors are connected to a fifty ohm load then the hybrid passes a fraction of the power passing forward through the unit to the other pair of connectors.

It is almost identical to the full Stockton Directional Wattmeter but in this case solely for QRP use. I.E. under 5 watt right up to 145MHz It has been tried with some success on 70Cms but the accuracy of our dummy load is questionable at this frequency.

It is bi-directional of course but in this application it uses just the one meter and a switch. Winding the cores is fairly easy providing you remember that once through the middle of the yellow core is one turn, Put 14 turns of the fine wire on the core and spread them evenly. Keep the wire tight, (it will be beneficial to use some bees wax or hot glue to hold the wire in place)

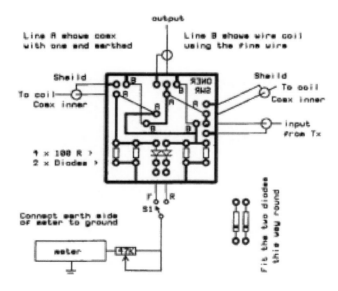

QRP SWR INDICATOR

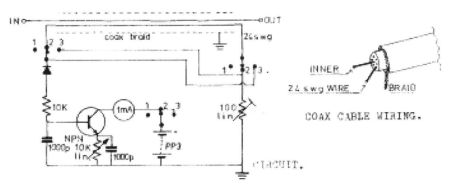

COAX CABLE WIRING.

CIRCUIT.

SWITCH: 1 = OFF,   2 = FORWARD,   3 = REVERSE.

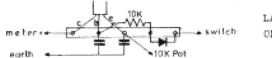

LAYOUT OF D.C. AMPLIFIER
ON 5 WAY TAG STRIP.

This simple indicator gives relative readings of forward and reverse aerial current, allowing forward readings for the peaking of output power and reverse readings for aerial matching purposes.

The bridge is based upon a random length (abt 18") of heavy duty AIR-SPACED coaxial cable. The ends are bared as shown, and a couple of feet of enamelled 24 swg wire (or similar) is carefully threaded through one of the air spacing holes.

The three leads must be insulated from each other - a 'mass' of PVC tape does the job! The 100 ohm preset is a reference impedance.

The forward and reverse currents are are rectified and fed into a simple NPN D.C. amplifier (any high gain transistor will serve). The gain of the amplifier forms a useful front panel control - increasing the gain for low current levels.

A front panel switch is used for OFF/FWD/REV and a PP3 provides the power.

Construction is not critical, a stout copper wire bus bar was put across the case to provide a decent earthing point and the D.C. Amplifier was built on a tag strip as shown.

The indicator was set up using a dummy load across the input, the gain control being useful for low reverse readings.

Two watts pushes the needle hard over with about two thirds gain, but this naturally depends upon the gain of the D.C. amplifier and the forward resistance of the diode.

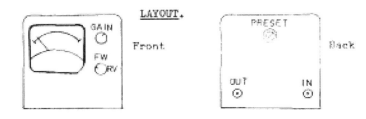

LAYOUT.

Front

Back

**GEORGE DOBBS
G3RJV
SPRAT 12
DECEMBER 1977**

QRP Z-MATCH ATU

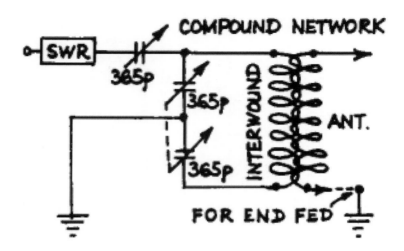

Having a centre fed zepp with a 44 feet top and trying to make an ATU to match it on all bands was quite a problem, what with a series or parallel tuning and trying to adjust the taps for best match, was not easy.

Looking through an old handbook I came across a Z match and it looked just what was needed.

L1 and L2 are wound on two inch plastic drain pipe and using 4mm plugs and sockets, a set of plug in coils were made for all bands. L1 is wound with 1.5mm solid wire and L2 with plastic covered flex. L2 is fully interleaved or layer wound with L1 and should be nearly the same number of turns. It is now possible to load up on all bands, and it also works fine on an end fed system.

For further details refer to the third edition of the RSGB Handbook or *Radio Communication*, July 1976.

GEORGE BURT
GM3OXX
SPRAT 25
WINTER 1980/1

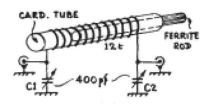

This QRP ATU was constructed from parts of old transistor radios and works extremely well, and has variable inductance and capacitance. The construction is as follows:-

The ferrite rod was stripped of original windings and then had a piece of notepaper wrapped around it. Once the paper was nearly into a tube, it was glued and finally rolled up into the complete tube, leaving the ferrite rod a sliding fit. The coil was then wound round the tube and fitted into a plastic box along with two small capacitors from the old radios. The unit was then wired to diagram. Operation is very straightforward like any other circuit, except that the inductance is completely variable by sliding the ferrite in and out of the tube.

I have used the ATU on 3.5MHz through 28MHz with very reasonable results. The first call to a station on 7MHz produced results using ten feet long wire indoors, ending up in a three-way between a station in Hull and one in Dublin using 2 watts PEP. Subsequent tests on better aerials have proved very reasonable and a 1:1 match can always be achieved.

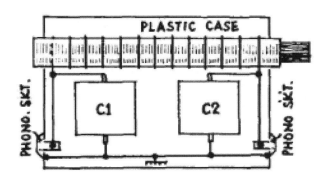

TONY HAAS
G4LDY
SPRAT 28
AUTUMN 1987

CAPACITIVE TUNING FOR LOOP AERIALS

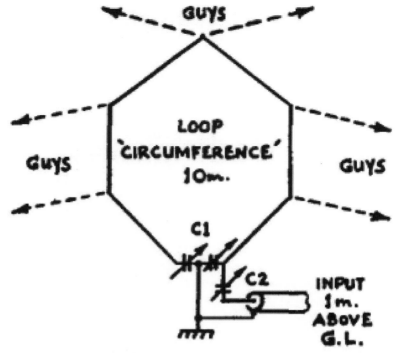

Reference the loop aerial described in the Winter issue of SPRAT, capacitive matching may be used as an alternative (Ref 1). During 1968 I experimented with a loop aerial using the matching arrangement shown in Fig 1. C1, a 500pF twin gang capacitor tunes the loop, and it is matched to the co-axial cable by means of a capacitive current divider which includes C2, a 50pF air spaced capacitor (direct matching to the output stage of a TTX is also possible using this method). With this arrangement an swr of 1:1 is easily obtained. Once the setting of C2 for a particular band has been found it need not be retuned but movement of frequency within the band will require readjustment of C1 to keep the loop in tune. This is because the loop is a very high Q circuit. I agree that most of the losses in the loop are due to the skin effect of the antenna conductor, so the larger the conductor surface the lower the losses. My loop was made from 17 cm wide copper foil, designed for screen windings in high power transformers. The circumference of the loop should be between 1/3 and 1/4 wavelength at the highest frequency to be used. Note that very high voltages are built up across the ends of the loop. Ordinary air spaced capacitors will usually handle QRP, but if flashover occurs use two sections in series to increase the voltage rating. The loop radiates at both high and low angles on sky wave, and is omnidirectional in this mode. Ground wave radiation is in the figure-of-eight pattern found with receiving loops. The aerial provides useful short and medium range communication where space is limited. For the higher frequencies I believe that even a short, loaded, vertical aerial would give better results and be simpler to erect and operate.

Ref 1. Down-to-earth Army Antenna, Electronics, August 21 1967

HA-JO BRANDT
DJ1ZB
SPRAT 25
WINTER 1980/1

A REAL QRPp VSWR METER

From ordinary VSWR meters it is well known that on a given aerial a higher VSWR is measured when using 100 watts instead of 10 watts of RF power. Therefore, to achieve correct results qrp operators should have a VSWR meter as sensitive as possible. At full sensitivity the meter described here will need less than 10 mW to reach the SET point, over the range 1.8 to 30 MHz. On the other hand, about 16 watts is the maximum permissible power, because the HPA 2800 diodes are driven to their maximum PIV ratings.

The Circuit

For better sensitivity, two current transformers are use, with 20 turns each, Their inductivity may differ, due to core tolerances, but should be about 450 uH or more. The division ratio of the capacitive divider C1/C2 is rather low and its total capacity high, to provide a low impedance source at 1.8 MHz. However, at 30 MHz this capacitance is too high to achieve a low VSWR in the 50 ohms line. This problem has been solved by incorporating this capacitance into a low pass filter with a cutoff frequency of about 40 MHz (Fig.1).

Screening

The 430 ohms load resistors across the current transformers cause a problem being not so critical with less sensitive VSWR meters having load resistors in the tens of ohms range: Stray coupling from the 50 ohms line into the diode circuit! To prevent this, the circuit diagram shows three different screened areas: (1) the 50 ohms line, (2) the area of the divided cable voltage, and (3) the area of the current transformers' output voltage.

Area 1 contains just the 50 ohms line, the current transformers T1, and the capacitors C1, C3 and C4. For the line the center conductor and insulation of a coaxial cable is used which just allows the current transofrmers to be slipped over its diameter. A screen between the transformer windings and the conductor has not been found necessary. A u-shaped metal plate acts as a screen for area 1. The leads from C1 and T1 leave this area through three holes in this metal cover.

Screening between areas 2 and 3 is not so critical. Both may be arranged on a common pcb. However, two separate metal bolts are used for grounding the current transformer leads and capacitor C2. Also, a grounded "guard ring" should be provided to separate the diode terminals belonging to either area 2 or 3 (Fig.2). The ground points for the blocking capacitors at the FWD and REF terminals are not critical. The pcb is fastened to one side of the u-shaped screen of area 1.

Alignment

A signal generator or a qrp transmitter with good harmonic suppression is needed, and 50 ohms termination. Firstly, trimmer C2 is set at 2/3 and C3 at 1/3 of full mesh. Due to the two current transformers there may be three initial states: The meter may operate right, it may operate right, but in the opposite direction, or forward and reverse indications may be equal. By reversing the polarity of one or both current transformers at "x" the correct connections must be tried out. Then C2 can be adjusted for minimum reverse indication at 14 MHz.

Then the low pass filter must be adjusted for minimum VSWR of the 50 ohms line up to 30 MHz. A sensitive VSWR meter like that to be built would be nice for this purpose (raising the old question what to be older, the hen or the egg), but normal resistive bridges are sufficiently sensitive for this job. The adjustment is done by tuning C3 and changing the turns spacing of Ls, and by inserting an optimum capacitor for C4 (depending on the capacitance of the coaxial jack itself). During the adjustments VSWR checks should be made on both directions, TX - ANT, and ANT - TX. OMs having access to a modern network analyzer will find that a return loss of about 30 dB can be achieved, and that the insertion loss of this VSWR meter will be about 0.2dB. Finally, C2 can be readjusted for minimum reverse indication at 28 or 30 MHz.

HA-JO BRANDT
DJ1ZB
SPRAT 69
WINTER 1991/2

Meter dial

For the indication of CSWR there are two choices to employ a meter. The first is to buy a 50uA or 100uA instrument and to draw an additional VSWR dial onto the uA dial. Assuming a linear diode characteristic, the formula $I = M.(\sqrt{S} - \sqrt{1/S})/(\sqrt{S} + \sqrt{1/S})$ may be used to calculate the current value for a specific VSWR. (S= VSWR; M=end value of meter dial).

The other way is to purchase a cheap or used VSWR meter, even if it were designed for CB purposes only, and to replace the whole internal RF circuitry. Then, however, some tests should be made with the instrument of this meter. Most cheap instruments carry a VSWR dial according to the formula mentioned above, but show a noticeable non linearity between current and deflection. From the formula it can be deduced that the meter current for the SET point must be three times the VSWR 2 current and two times the VSWR 3 current. On many cheap instruments, the real SET point will be found at about 80% of full deflection, and therefore a new SET mark should be drawn there.

Ferrites

From correspondance I know that, depending on the market situation, members may have difficulties to obtain the Amidon FT50B-43 core. As the inductivity and the turns number of the current transformer is given, one may try to substitute other materials. For RF nickel zinc ferrites like the Amidon 43 or 61 materials are to be preferred. Most high permeability ferrites, however, are magnesium zinc, and tend to get hot in high power applications. This may not be critical in qrp operation. If it should be impossible with other cores to reproduce the inductivity of 450 uH, the parallel load resistor must also be reduced, with consequent losses in sensitivity. The general relation is that the inductive reactance of the current transformer should be at least ten times the load resistor, at the lowest operating frequency.

Ls   5 turns 10mm inner diameter, self supporting, 1mm dia wire, spaced to about 15mm length.
C2 & C3   Philips 110pF foil trimmers.   C1 & C4   Ceramic disc capacitors 400v.
T1   20 turns PTFE insulated 0.5mm dia. 'wire wrap' wire on Amidon FT50B-43 core [FairRite part 5943001901]   [1] [2] [3] are the Shielded Sections : See Text

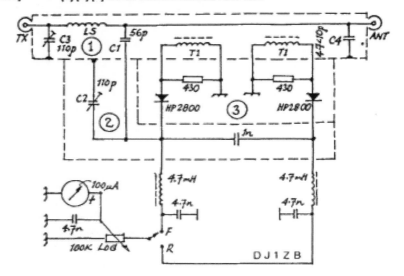

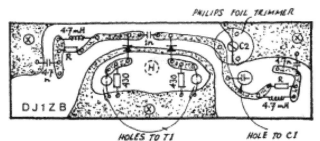

"H" = LOCATION OF HOLE IF SINGLE CURRENT TRANSFMR.
USED FOR OTHER VSWR METER DESIGNS.
"X" = 3 HOLES FOR GROUND BOLTS.
"R" = 18K RESISTOR SOMETIMES REQUIRED TO IMPROVE REF.
MINIMUM, AT LOWEST FREQUENCY.

FURTHER NOTES ON THE QRPp VSWR METER

The construction of a second version of this device revealed a problem which led to a slight modification of the original circuit. When trying to align the meter it was impossible to get a better reflected minimum that S=1,2. Comparing the differences in the construction of the first and the second version, the problem has obviously been aggravated by the smaller cross section of the screened area 1. In the first version, this section was 30 by 30 millimetres, but in the second just 16 by 20 millimetres. This led to an additional capacitive load for the 430 ohms resistors across the current transformers, causing some phase shift of the r.f. voltage generated. Luckily however, the whole construction could be saved by introducing another phase shift in the capacitive divider, by inserting a small resistor in series to the 56 pF capacitor. When a potentiometer of 47 of 100 ohms is used at first for this purpose, an exact null can be achieved even at 30 MHz by alternate alighting of this resistor and capacitor C2. Then this resistor is measured and replaced by a suitable fixed value, and the alignment repeated by adjusting C2 alone.

For the second version, the optimum value had been 39 ohms. After this solution had been found, the first version was investigated again to see if any improvement could be reached. Here the best obtainable minimum had been S = 1,05 at 30 MHz. By inserting a potentiometer it was also possible to get an exact minimum, and the optimum resistor value was found to be 22 ohms.

For safety reasons, the dissipation rating of this resistor should be in the 0.5 to 1 watts range. The maximum dissipation will be needed when the maximum power of about 16 watts at 30 MHz is applied to the meter. Therefore, the general aim must be to need a resistor as small as possible for correct alignment, and this can be achieved by a construction maintaining a parasitic capacitance across the current transformers as small as possible. For a general relief of this problem, the load resistor of the current transformers could be reduced to 390 ohms or even less, but this would also lower the maximum sensitivity of this meter (about 5 mW for full deflection to the SET point).

**HA-JO BRANDT
DJ1ZB
SPRAT 71
SUMMER 1992**

FIELD STRENGTH METER

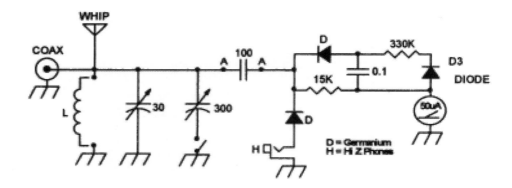

I built this "instrument" some weeks ago during an antenna test.
In my laboratory I did not have a FSM and I could not test transmitters or antennas effectively on the air, especially compared with know values of other devices.
For example I wasn't able to compare an antenna vs a reference antenna or the gain by receiving a standard signal whit two antennas under test.

With this instrument all tests become easy, moreover I can listen an eventual modulated signal via a simple diode detection circuit, the audio can be heard with high impedance headphones or injected to an LM386 standard BF amplifier (circuit shown). An RF amplifier can be added if more sensitivity is requested.

The full HF band and VHF up to 50 MHz can be covered with a set of coils. I used some old Grid dip meter coils but can be easily built.
A micro-switch on the CV permits us to switch HF or VHF ranges by adding a higher capacitance section to the low capacitance section of the CV.

MARCO ELEUTERI
IK0VSV
SPRAT 119
SUMMER 2004

And old analogue tester
indicator is used as meter and
the large size permits me to see
easily some meters away - this
is important when testing an
antenna.

The pickup circuit is from an
old "stomophone" RF test
instrument for repeaters field
maintenance service very easy
to "clone" with the same characteristics.

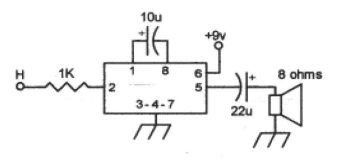

COIL DATA
1) 80 turns 0.5mm on 20mm insulated core   (approx 1-4 MHz)
2) 20 turns as above (approx 4-15 MHz)
3) 10 turns as above (approx 8 to 25 MHz)
4) 5 turns 2 mm spaced (approx 20-50 MHz)

To measure on UHF region or broadband mode, don't connect the Coil.
The sensitivity is less but good.
The schematic is very simple but very sensitive, all diodes must be germanium.

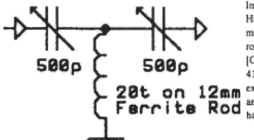

500p   500p
20t on 12mm
Ferrite Rod

Inspired by the article in the G QRP Club Circuit
Handbook p. 65 by Tony Haas, G4LDY, I built a
mini-match using the same variable inductor : a ferrite
rod sliding in a former.   Tony's circuit was a Pi-Filter
[Collins] but mine is a T-Filter because of my end-fed
41.4m wire, 7m high. My experience is that it gives
excellent results. On 80, 40 and 20m I can tune my
antenna to 1:1 SWR. The rod fully in the coil on 80,
half way on 40 and out of the former on 20.

NO COST ATU MKII

The ferrite rod has a diameter of 8mm
and the coil is wound on a plastic tube
9mm inner diameter [12mm outer] about
8cm long. The 20 turns occupy a length
of 4cm. The two variable capacitors are
of the polyvaricon type used in broadcast
AM radios.   Both variable capacitors
must be insulated from ground. The case
is homemade from two U-shaped parts.

GUSTAV MICHALIK
DL6FBQ
SPRAT 71
SUMMER 1992

TWIN QRP RF METER

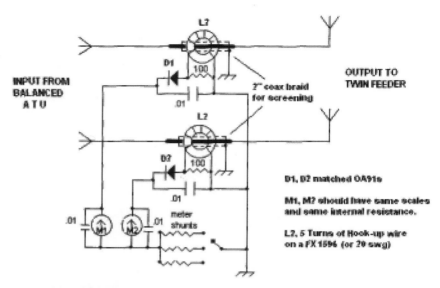

INPUT FROM
BALANCED
A T U

L?

D1

100

.01

2" coax braid
for screening

OUTPUT TO
TWIN FEEDER

L2

D?

100

.01

.01 M1   M2 .01

meter
shunts

D1, D2 matched OA91s

M1, M2 should have same scales
and same internal resistance.

L2, 5 Turns of Hook-up wire
on a FX 1596 (or 20 swg)

CIRCUIT DESCRIPTION The idea is not new. It first came to my notice in Technical Topics, Radcom, October 1999. But what I have tried to do is make a general purpose unit from the basic idea. One need only use half the circuit, if only one meter is required.

The heart of the unit is the transformer. With the values chosen it is easy to calculate what the power should be. If the primary is 1 turn (i.e. one feeder passed through the core) and the secondary is 5 turns, there will be a 1:5 current reduction from primary to secondary. This current can be measured by placing a load across the secondary and measuring the voltage. I have chosen 100ohms which indicates a voltage of 4.5 with 5 watts into 50 ohms passing through the transformer primary. At .5w the measured voltage was 1.5. A 500 micro-amp meter will be more than adequate to read full scale deflection at these low powers. Three different shunts may be necessary to allow for the different ranges of feeder impedance. very much less current will be observed at 600 ohms than at 50 for example. It would be possible to calibrate these meters in RF amperes but it becomes complicated with rms and peak values. I have therefore left them as a rough guide in calibration by comparing them with a known RF ammeter scale and load. (Or you can work out what the current should be with Ohms Law). But the meters do tell me that I have maximum power going into the antenna and that the feeder is balanced at the start. N.B. it is possible to have 1:1 SWR reading with not much RF going into the antenna! Especially with a Z Match.

Values of meter shunts are not given because of the variation of internal meter resistances. This must be left to the builder as to what he might have in the junk box and calculate the shunts accordingly. A simple circuit for measuring meter resistance is given in the ARRL handbook 1984, chapter 16.2.

JIMMY BOLTON
G3HBN
SPRAT 119
SUMMER 2004

Putting the balancing transformer at the input rather than the output of the tuner will reduce losses considerably, which is of paramount importance for QRP. Originally I used an ex R7 vertical 1:1 transformer, but had other uses for it, so I decided to go for a cheap, yet effective alternative transformer.

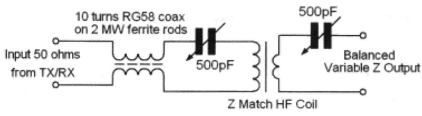

40 - 10m Balanced Tuner

Just take a MW transistor radio ferrite rod, split it and superglue them. Then wind 7 turns (for 40m-10m) of RG58 coax - you have a 1:1 transformer ! Rather than using the classic T configuration, I decided to experiment with a classic Z Match HF coil, and the result was a very broad tuned ATU that can match most impedances.

The coil is 5 turns each, 14 s w g wire tightly wound, each turn spaced 1/4 inch . The primary winding 2.6 inches and the secondary 3 inches diameter. If you like to include the lower bands, try increasing the coax turns to 12, and use the LF Z Match coil, which is the same dimensions but 8 turns for the primary and 6 turns for the secondary. This has not been tested though, as my main interest is 40-20-15 meters.

**PAUL DEBONO
9H1FQ
SPRAT 127
SUMMER 2006**

BALUN SWITCHER AND FEEDER STRAPPER

Most of my antennas have used balanced feeders of open wire or 300 ohm line. I have built and experimented with several types of ATU to feed these antennas. ATUs often incorporate a balun at the output to feed into the line.

This arrangement usually works well but sometimes the best way to match the antenna on a particular band is to switch out the balun and strap the feeders together. In most of my ATUs I incorporate the following circuit to make it easier to do.

Each ATU has an insulated ? inch stereo jack socket wired as shown.
An insulated jack plus with tip and ring shorted together is plugged in to disconnect the balun and strap the feeders. When the plug is out the balun is in circuit and connected in the usual way.

The jack socket has
6 connections on each side
looking at the underside from the front

tip	1 O	O 4	
ring	2 O	O 5	
common	3 O	O 6	

**IAN BROWN
G3TLH
SPRAT 126
SUMMER 2006**

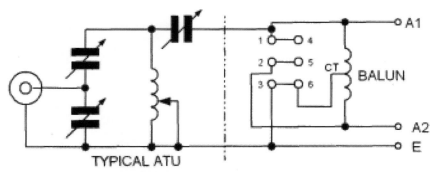

Plug Out - Operation with Balun & Balanced Feeders

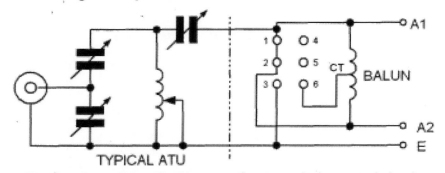

Plug In - Operation with Strapped Feeders - Balun out of circuit

With the plug out 1 – 4, 2 – 5 and 3 – 6 are connected together. With the plug in the plug tip, ring and common connect to 1, 2 and 3 respectively and 1 – 4, 2 – 5 and 3 – 6 get disconnected.

Also the plug is wired to short tip and ring terminals 1 and 2 together.
This provides a convenient method of balun switching and feeder strapping simply by inserting the plug. Removing the plug reverts to normal operation with the balun in circuit.

The circuits below show the wiring of the socket and connections to the ATU and balun with the plug out and with the plug inserted.

- With the plug out terminals A1 and A2 connect to the balanced line.
- With the plug in terminals A1 and A2w are shorted and the balanced feeders are strapped.

In this configuration the ATU may also be used with a single antenna connected to either A1 or A2.

A lightweight inexpensive inverted vee dipole for portable operation, adapted from the BIC Flame-thrower from Fred Turpin, K6MDJ. Radiator wires are attached to insulators by passing them through clearance holes and knotting. Coax passes through clearance hole drilled in end of pipe cap and soldered to dipole wires. Seal around coax with model aeroplane cement then fill cap with epoxy. Cup hook screws into epoxy to hang the antenna.

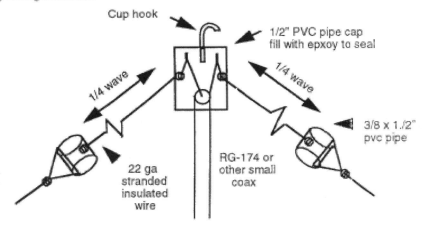

Cup hook

1/2" PVC pipe cap
fill with epxoy to seal

1/4 wave

1/4 wave

3/8 x 1./2"
pvc pipe

22 ga
stranded
insulated
wire

RG-174 or
other small
coax

JOE EVERHART
N2CX
SPRAT 93
WINTER 1997/8

A BALUN FOR THE LDG AUTOMATIC TUNER OR OTHER ANTENNA TUNER

This simple addition to the LDG QRP Tuner allows it to feed a balanced antenna with a ratio of 4:1 or 1:1. Before I made one I tried what was on the bench! It has 8 <u>twisted</u> trifilar turns on an unknown toroid, but I think it is an FT50-43. It tunes my doublet easily on 9 bands from 1.8-30MHz with no sign of stress or heating.

It is mounted inboard with a 3 way switch and 2 terminals. I found a switch small enough to fit the back panel of the LDG Tuner giving three positions : Direct / 1:1 / 4:1.

Using my QRP++ I have worked a selection of DX including VE8TA & ZP6CW on 18MHz CW, K0HA, VE3KZ, SV5/IK2YYO on 18MHz SSB and a heap of EU on all bands.

PF LINSLEY
G3PDL
SPRAT 96
AUTUMN 1998

LDG TUNER BALUN UPDATE

A much simpler way to switch G3PDL's Balun [SPRAT 96 - p.19] after the LDG Automatic Tuner uses only a SPDT, Centre-Off [on-off-on] toggle switch. This is cheaper and easier to find that a miniature wafer switch. [See Diagram]

The centre-off switch position is used for coax or long wire. The 1:1 and 4:1 positions are used for balanced feeders.

This works because only one antenna will be connected at a time. The tiny toggle switch needs much less room than a rotary switch.

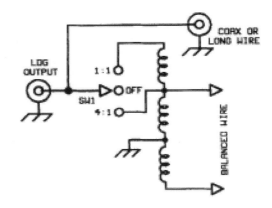

FRANK BRUMBAUGH
W4LJD
SPRAT 97
WINTER 1998/9

Having experimented with various forms of twinlead, ladderline and other commercial balanced feeder, the need for economical and robust line drove the effort to home brew my own. It seemed that most twinlead lacked strength and suffered fatally from wind-whipping. 450-ohm "window line", while more robust, still suffered from wind and ice loading. Both de-tuned significantly with rain and ice, esp. with high SWR antennas like the Lazy-H. The cost of commercial spreaders for 600-ohm (and higher) "open" line put them out of reach since I was making antennas like Sterba Curtains for instance, and feeding them from 250' down the hill. A real drain on the feeder/frustration budget.

Most articles on the subject suggested spreaders of waxed or lacquered wood, PVC pipe, lucite (perspex) blocks, even plastic forks. All were big in terms of weight and ice loading, not to mention fabrication problems. Considering the needs of robust ladderline, it occurred to me that there really isn't a great deal of lateral force on the conductors, so all I have to worry about is keeping them from ripping apart.

The nylon inspiration struck one hot afternoon while re-loading my weed-wacker*. The line is strong, durable, - and cheap! After trying several variants the following version seems to provide the combination of performance, reliability and economy that fits my needs. Note that while I chose 600-ohm line, you can follow the guidelines in the ARRL Handbook to make any other impedance you'd like.

Materials and techniques described here represent a lot of trial-and-error and variations should be carefully considered. You may be able to improve on this, (and I hope you do), so treat this as a starting point rather than the ultimate solution. By all means share your knowledge and experience.

Twelve-Step-Program to 600-ohm (nominal) balanced feedline:

1.) #16 or #18 wire, bare or insulated.   (0.051/0.040 inch, 18/19SWG, 1.27/1.01mm – G3MFJ)
2.) Roll of 95 mil round weed-wacker line.
3.) Cut wacker line to 4" lengths while enjoying libation, snacks, TV.
4.) Bend nylon ends around a small hot solder iron tip. Make ½" hooks with i.d. to fit your line conductors. Use gloves, more libation, etc.
5.) Make two 4' stakes with plywood "T" near top, with notches 3.5" apart.
6.) Pound the stakes into the ground, about 30' apart.
7.) Unwind the spool of wire & double it. Stretch it through stake slots.
8.) Tension the wire with concrete blocks on ground outside of the stakes.
9.) Hook spreaders on the wire 12-18" apart, then hot melt glue in place, using a "saddle-blob" over both sides of the loops and wire.
10) Use hot air gun to remove glue stringers and melt glue to wire.
11) Advance your ladderline to the next segment. Roll up made section.
12) Happily apply your 250' of prime, lo-loss feeder/phasing line!

*(Note by G3MFJ – a 'weed-wacker' is the US term for a petrol engine driven grass/weed trimmer – sometimes known in the UK as a 'strimmer'. This uses thicker line than a domestic electric-motor driven model – US grass is probably tougher than the UK equivalent!)

SEAB LYON
AA1MY
SPRAT107
SUMMER 2001

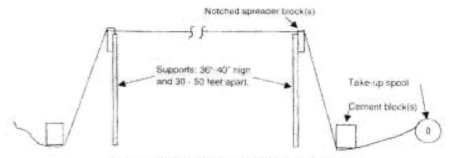

Fig. 1. Tensioning Fixture for Ladder-Line fabrication.
Keeping line under tension helps keep spreaders in place while gluing.
Notches in blocks are wider than spreaders to maintain width tension.

Fig. 2. Spreaders are hooked over the wire, then hot-melted to it.
Spreaders are spaced 12"-18" depending on amount of twist anticipated.
Hook all the spreaders on first; adjust the spacing; then glue them. Ensure
that glue bonds securely to at least 1/4" of wire and fits the spreader loops.

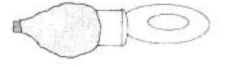

Fig. 3. Robust Wire Terminations.
Ring Lugs are crimped, soldered, then
blobbed with hot-melt glue to reduce
flex fatigue failures.

Notes: (practice, practice, practice)

Melting/smoking nylon won't ruin solder tips, but your marriage ... hmmm.

Stranded wire for low-stress segments, solid for higher-stress.

Use "heavy-duty" (if available) hot melt glue for best cold wx & U-V tolerance.

"Batch-process" spacers, etc. for efficiency. (~170 for 250' of line)

Blob more hot melt glue on the end terminations to prevent flex failures.

Application Hint:

I pre-cut 1/2 wave sections of it as well as 1/4 & ½-wave single wires (for a couple of bands) and crimp/solder ring lugs on the ends. That enables spur-of-the-moment-bolt-together assembly of an amazing assortment of antenna types. It brings great joy to lift an idea from such green pastures as W4RNL's web page and actually build a killer antenna in an afternoon – even on windy, freezing, rainy days! Balanced Tuners have become objects of great interest thanks again to L.B. Cebik's remarkable body of work on his now-famous web page.

The Ken Maxted [GM4JMU] RF Current Transformer [SPRAT 52] is better than my RF Sniffer [SPRAT 51] because it is loaded with a resistance and will indicate at a current loop only

BUT- if you are testing a feeder and aerial outside to find where the current loops are, you have an impossible job with slotted ribbon feeder as you cannot slip on the toroid - as is true of any open wire feeder with spacers

My idea of slotting the ferrite toroid gets over this, you can hook the thing anywhere on the wire - add Ken's loading resistance and you have a handy gadget.

BUT- ferrite is as hard as glass, you can eventually hacksaw through it, but end up with a worn-out blade or ruined needle file and a slot so narrow as to admit nothing thicker than about 20 swg - useless on slotted ribbon or thick wires.

The solution took a long time to hit me:

a] Scratch the toroid with a tile cutter or glass cutter on the diameter

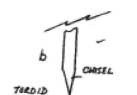

b] Tap it on the core with a wee sharp cold chisel and hammer and it splits open neatly into two halves

Now take the halves to a hand grindstone [or I suppose any machine buff] You will find that two of the broken ends can be ground down with 'nea bother'.

They now fit together as shown.
The fracture is now cemented with a tiny drop of super glue [cyanoacrylate glue]
The glue line does not affect the magnetic properties of the toroid

RONNIE MARSHALL
GM4JJG
SPRAT 71
SUMMER 1992

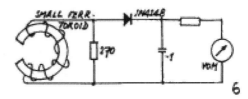

So Ken's useful device becomes as shown:

It will let you test an ATU for best current in the aerial and allow to mess about outside checking for balanced currents on feeders and currents loops in the right place on an aerial

Put the toroid into a piece of perspex tubing [or similar] and add checks of Formica thus:
This means that the wire is always in the centre of the core and gives constant coupling for accurate comparisons - useful in tuning up an aerial.

HELPING THE MAST STAY UP

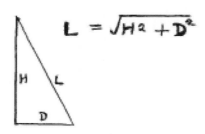

$$L = \sqrt{H^2 + D^2}$$

The formula shown to the left allows one to calculate the mast to stay picket length. At least 3 feet (1m) should be added to allow for connection to the mast and the stay picket. The longer one can make D the more effective the stay. Try and design your stay system for unexpectedly high winds as this will give you a safety factor. We suggest four stays in each set. For masts up to 9m we suggest two sets of stays, one attached to the top of the mast and one at a height of Hx0.6.=H2. Higher masts should have three sets of stays, the third set beig fitted at a height of H2x0.6..We suggest that the stays be made from polypropylene rope of a suitable breaking strain. This rope is non-stretch, and it seems to last for ever. The same is true of masts made from plug-together strong plastic sections if you can get hold of them.

AAA TECHNICAL STAFF
SPRAT 112
AUTUMN 2002

USING CO-AX TO FORM A TUNED FEEDER

THE USE OF TWO CO-AXIAL CABLES TO FORM A TUNED FEEDER HAS lead to much experimental work, particularly by DJoGD,DL2RM, DJ1ZB, and of course Gi4rCY. As already reported, feeders of this type introduce some 20 % of power loss (about 1 dB). At powers up to around 100 watts this presents no problem, but DL2RM reports that if 500 watts is applied for several minutes there is some heating of the cable, which would obviously become worse if the cable was buried (DL2RM wishes to use the system as an invisible feeder to remote antennas). Ha-Jo,DJ1ZB, gave up the Winter Sports to allow him to spend his Christmas holiday investigating the problem. As a result of this work he has produced a very scholarly paper of some 3,000 words on the subject. It is too long to print in SPRAT, but copies can be obtained from G8PG (UK 3 first class stamps, overseas 3 ircs). Ha-Jo made measurements every 500 kHz over a wide range of frequencies, and his most important findings are as follows. The two halves of a doublet are very often not balanced because they are erected over areas of different earth conductivity (this presumably applies to all doublets).Balance should be obtained by measuring the resonant frequency of each half separately, and trimming the top of one half until both halves resonate at the same frequency. The currents in the two cables forming the feeder are better balanced if the screens are earthed to the atu via a 100 ohm resistor. Matching problems only occur when there is low impedance at the TX end of the feeder combined with high parallel capacitance. The worst matching problems occur when a top showing high impedance at the operating frequency is connected to a feeder a quarter wavelength long. Matching is much easier when the centre of the doublet is at low impedance. Matching is further eased by using 75 ohm co-ax rather than the 50 ohm variety (this is because an important element in determining impedance is the square of the co-axial cable impedance. Thus for low power work 93 ohm cable such as RG62 or RG71 would be even better. If it is not available the next best is 75 ohm low loss TV cable). The use of 50 ohm cable should be avoided, and its use may explain some of the poor results previously reported. To further ensure ease of matching the top should be pf a length which is not resonant at any band in use (the Gi4PCY 175 foot top is an example). Current balance is also important and worth experimenting with . The best coupling device is a really well balanced, symmetric atu. Twin 75 ohm ,low loss cable is available in Germany, but expensive. The cheap 3 KW,75 ohm cable once available on the Berlin black market has disappeared — the Red Army has gone home! Finally, DL2RM points out that with the rising concern about exposure to rf fields the use of this type of feeder on higher power stations, both commercial and amateur, may be of increasing importance. Again sincere thanks to all involved in this work. It is an excellent example of the strength of applied engineering knowledge within our Club.

GUS TAYLOR
G8PG
SPRAT 80
AUTUMN 1994

BALANCED FEEDER MOD FOR T-MATCH ATUS

When modifying a T-Match ATU (such as the MFJ ATU) for balanced feeder, the use of a 4 to 1 balun on the output side is bad practice and can lead to losses, it is much better to place the balun on the input side, and if it is a choke balun it will make the ATU balanced, if not grounded, I know that the purists will say a wood or plastic box should be used , but in practice I have found that the balance is good.

I have a 1 to 1 choke balun on the input side made by winding 20 turns RG58U coax on each of 2 ferrite rods in series, and on the output side I use the coax socket to feed the balanced output. The only drawback is a slight hand capacity but I can tune every band including 50 MHz and don't use QRO as you could get an RF burn from the case, no trouble with QRP. No earth should be connected, unless coax feeder is used.

T SORBIE
GM3MXN
SPRAT 103
SUMMER 2000

A LYNX CENTRE PIECE

The domed plastic (black) cap from a "Lynx" deodorant can is an exact fit on 40mm, white, waste water pipe (as used as an outlet from sinks etc.) The cap is unusually well made from two concentric tubes and the waste pipe fits exactly between the two tubes and with a smear of Evostick or silicone rubber makes a good waterproof cover. Two caps and a short offcut of pipe can make a good trap container or dipole centre.

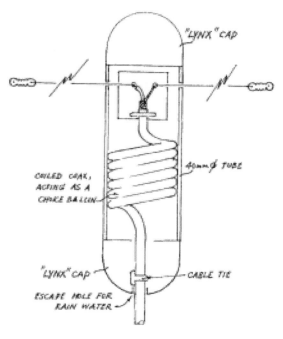

MA EALES
G7SGF
SPRAT 86
SPRING 1996

A FEW THOUGHTS ON ANTENNA SUPPORTS

Firstly, a quick but very important word about towers and high commercially made masts. Assuming you have planning permission to erect one, do realise that erecting it safely and ensuring it stays safe is a civil engineering job. Follow the instructions given by the makers very carefully, and if you have any doubts about your ability to do any part of the job call in a reliable expert. Also make sure you have full insurance cover during erection and subsequent use. If you intend to work on a tower make sure you have a hard hat, safety harness and tool belt. Then read the safety section of the ARRL Antenna Book before starting work. When working on high towers remember that death is permanent!

Smaller, lighter structures up to about 40 feet high can be home made and safely erected provided care is taken. Probably the most famous design is the A Frame, which goes back at least 60 years. Figure 1 illustrates its construction. It will help us examine some useful points. The A frame and topmast are of the same length, made from suitable timber. Fore and aft guys are attached to the top of the A section, and 3 guys are spaced 90° around the topmast: the weight of the antenna acts as a fourth guy. The bottom of the mast rests on the ground, so it must be weatherproofed by giving it several coats of creosote, then wrapping it in metal foil. The guys should be made from non-stretch plastic rope such as polypropelene of at least 400 lbs breaking strain. Similar rope is used for the halyards. These pass through suitable metal or plastic rings (not pulleys) attached to the top of the mast. Always fit at least one spare ring and halyard. Tie the ends of the halyard together to

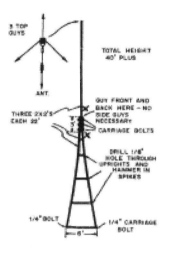

Figure 1. (With thanks to A.R.R.L.)
The mast is "walked up" against two stakes driven into the ground. Leave in place. Rot proof if wooden.

make an endless loop. The guys are attached to wooden or metal stakes driven into the ground; if you use wood rot proof it. One problem found with this design is that in very high wind gusts it can break just above the A section. Bolting a strengthening piece of timber between points X on the diagram overcomes the problem. Finally, a few general points about masts. Each set of guys improves wind resistance by about 20 mph/30 kph. If several sets of guys are used space them assymetrically on the mast to prevent mechanical resonances. The further away from the bottom of the mast you anchor a guy the more effective it is. If you use a wooden pole instead of a mast try and fit it on a tabernacle . If you have to bury the butt in the ground make the depth of the hole at least one tenth the height of the pole. Rot proof the butt and if possible fit one set of guys. Always carefully paint wooden structures to weatherproof them.

GUS TAYLOR
G8PG
SPRAT 92
AUTUMN 1997

EXTRA-LIGHT WEATHERPROOF DIPOLE SPACER

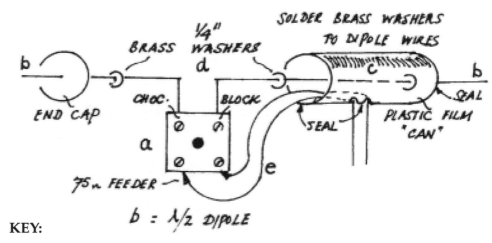

b = λ/2 DIPOLE

KEY:

a] Small choc block. b] Dipole wires. c] Plastic 35mm film canister.
d] ¼″ brass washers. e] 75 ohm feeder.

1] Solder brass washers to dipole wires.
2] Seal points of entry with waterproof sealant.

BERT FROGATT
G3SOX
SPRAT 97
WINTER 1998/9

MINI T-PIECE FOR DIPOLES

With purpose-made, ceramic T-pieces almost unobtainable nowadays, and heavy to boot, a lightweight, strong, small and cheap alternative can be adapted for those using small diameter coax cable of 31/2 or 5mm diameter.
The units used are sold in packages of six and are type RTT6 Garden Mesh Supports, manufactured by "Rainbow" (Gardener's Workshop).
After baring coax leads, and soldering to elements wires, they should be wrapped in plastic insulating tape, then bound with heavy-gauge wax thread. The joints should then be a tight fit inside the T-piece.
The exposed top end can then be sealed with waterproof "Bostik".
Stockist are Woolworth, and similar gardeners' suppliers.

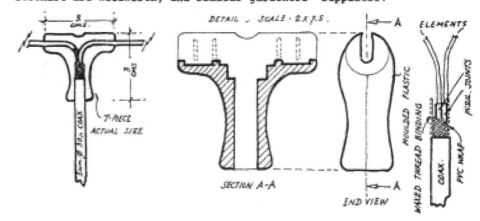

AW MCNEILL
G3FCK
SPRAT 64
AUTUMN 1990

Especially when operating portable, qrp rigs are often used with very high antennas which are not available to the average ham living in a city. Such antennas are excellent on transmit, of course, but their receiving energy is so high that it will overload even the doubly balanced mixer recommended earlier.

Therefore, an attentuator in the receiver input lead must be used. The author prefers T or Pi attenuators to simple potentiomter controls, because the match will remain constant on both sides independantly of the attenuation, and the resonance of the antennas and associated antenna tuners will not change.

Fig.9. shows a 0-10-20-30 dB step attenuator for Z= 50 ohms and its wiring arrangement around a 4x3 contact switch. The third portion is not used for switching, but as supports for the cable shield and the 4.7nF capacitor which is necessary for CD blocking of the HW7 RIT circuitry.

The switch can be mounted on the rear panel of the HW7 cabinet over the antenna jack. The rf cable to the receiver input is removed from points Q and S and soldered to the attenuator output. For connecting Q and S to the attenuator input a short new cable must be installed. The conjunction of the two cable shield on the switch should not be grounded.

Such an attenuator is also used by the author at the antenna input of his 0-T-2 FET regenerative receiver (see SPRAT Autumn 1975)

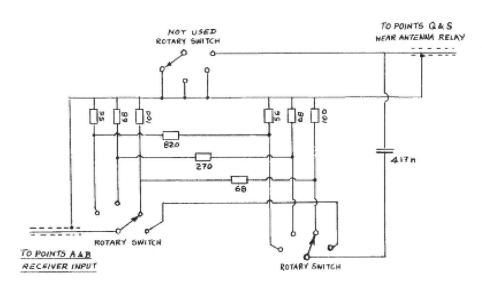

RECEIVER ANTENNA ATTENUATOR 0...30dB
FoR HW7 (AND OTHER RECEIVERS)

HA-JO BRANDT
DJ1ZB
SPRAT 10
SPRING 1977

SLED KITE

I find this a more reliable sky hook than The Delta Kite I was using last year. It is made far easier than The Delta and will cope with a much wider range of wind speeds. It goes up from the hand and when the required length of line has been paid out, can be pegged down and does not require any further attention.

This form of kite is known as a Sled Kite and has many variations, and some are more reliable than others. The design enclosed has been used as a pattern and about 60 have been made for the local children — it flies without any complication and at a high angle. It just goes up and can be quite a handful to get down in a fresh wind.

The sail is cut from bin liner and re-inforced with 1 inch wide adhesive plastic tape each side and eyeleted at attachment points (many bin liners are less than 36 inches deep). The sticks are about 3/16 inch square and fixed with short strips of 1 inch plastic adhesive tape each 9 inches and an additional strip at each end over the sticks and stuck to each side of the sail. The bottom end of the stick is fixed 1 inch in from the corner. The bridle 5 feet legs into 6 x ¼ x 1/16 inches spreader and 20 pound breaking strain swivel (obtainable from fishing tackle shops). The bridle is made from 20 pound braided nylon fishing line.

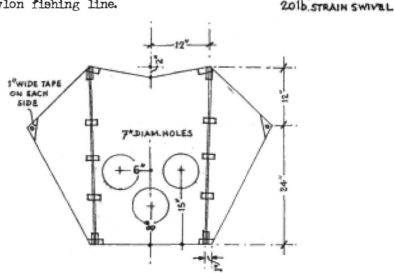

ROY ROWNTREE
G3ZQA
SPRAT 30
SPRING 1982

The use of a loaded whip aerial for HF portable operation is often convenient and for mobile operation it is almost universal. Such a whip is normally constructed to present a low impedance at its base where it is fed by means of co-axial cable. This arrangement has a number of disadvantages, including:-

1. A good earth connection or the use of radials is desirable.
2. The very low impedance can cause matching problems.
3. Normally, only one band operation is possible without changing the loading coil.
4. The aerial has a very small band width which restricts the choice of usable frequencies within the band.
5. The use of a capacitance hat* will further reduce the bandwidth of the aerial.

By constructing the whip to present a high impedance at its base and tuning by means of a pi-coupler between the transceiver and the base of the aerial, the following advantages occur:-

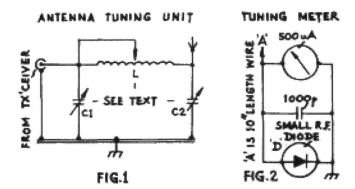

FIG.1   FIG.2

1. Neither an earth connection or the use of radials is necessary.
2. There are no matching problems.
3. Multi band operation is possible.
4. Instead of changing the physical length of the aerial, tuning is carried out at the pi-coupler and the whole of an amateur band can be covered without the need for any physical adjustment to the length of the aerial.
5. A capacitance hat* does not reduce the band width.
6. Since physical length is not so important for tuning, it is possible to increase the length of the whip (by one or two metres) under static conditions, i.e. vehicle not in motion, with greatly improved results.

CHAS BRYANT
GW3SB
SPRAT 30
SPRING 1982

Any whip aerial, home or commercially made, which was intended for low impedance feed on 3.5MHz will work on 7, 14, 21 and 28MHz with high impedance feed. The cheapest arrangement is to wrap 66 feet of wire around a garden cane and add the longest whip that will remain upright – if possible with a hat. A more sophisticated arrangement is to use a one inch diameter plastic water pipe, strengthened with a wooden dowel. Small staples may be driven in to hold the wire in place. Two-thirds of the wire should be close wound and the top one third should be spaced the equivalent of about a turn. This can be done quite simple by inter-winding plastic clothes line between the turns. The top may be a telescopic whip or jointed ex-wartime rod aerials (if still available). The author uses a sponge sandwich baking tin (stolen from the kitchen) for a capacitance hat. Lengths are unimportant but the higher the better. The author uses about two feet of whip for mobile operation and about nine feet for portable operation.

A suitable ATU is shown in Fig. 1, the values of the components will vary with different installations, but for 7MHz and above L might consist of 25 turns on a 1½ inch diameter former; C1 500pF and C2 100pF. For use on 3.5MHz it would probably be necessary to double these values. Both the position of the tap on L and the tuning of C2 are very critical. until an optimum position for the tap has been found, it is desirable to be able to move it one turn at a time, the use of a roller coaster would be ideal. It may be desirable to provide a slow motion drive for C2 as this will not only assist the very fine tuning required but also avoid accidental detuning due to vibration when the vehicle is in motion.

The method of adjustment is to tune the transmitter with a dummy load, then adjust the ATU for maximum signal in the receiver and, finally with the transmitter on for very short periods, adjust the ATU (not forgetting the tap on L as well as C1 and C2) for maximum voltage at the base of the aerial. The simple tuning meter, shown in Fig. 2, is suitable for this purpose. The short piece of wire A is placed near the base of the aerial and the ATU adjusted for maximum reading. It should be remembered that this is only a tuning indicator and that it does not indicate field strength. It cannot, therefore, be used to compare radiation on one band with that on another and the actual reading is of no significance.

* The author has found that a capacitance hat will increase signal strength by as much as one "S" point and, more important for QRP operation, a greater proportion of calls result in contacts.

We all know how unreliable magnetic compasses are. The earth's magnetic poles are always moving around, and the magnetic polarity of the earth's magnet flips every now and again. They are also affected by nearby magnetic objects and electric currents. This compass allows a true N-S line to be found on any sunny day, in spite of magnetic variation or deviation, it is as accurate as you make it, and won't drain your batteries. Compasses similar to this were originally used by the Vikings more than a thousand years ago. British and American forces used sun compasses in the desert during WWII.

Instructions:

1. Photocopy the graph and glue or pin the copy onto a flat piece of wood about 6mm thick. (You can reduce or enlarge it.)
2. Knock a nail through the wood in the centre of the graph so that it is more-or-less perpendicular to the wood.
3. Cut off the nail so that the portion sticking out of the wood is the same length as one division on the radial scale, and sharpen the tip to a point with a file.
4. Bend the nail, if necessary, so that the tip is vertically above the centre of the graph, when looking down on the graph. (The tip is the only significant point on the gnomon.) Of course, aluminium sheet can be used instead of wood for the base, and a screw instead of a nail allows the gnomon to be easily adjusted in length.

Using the orientation device:

On a sunny day….

1. Hold the base so that it is level. Several methods can be used to make it level: a bubble level, rolling ball bearing or gymbal arrangement or float the device in still water or you can try guessing! My bubble level was obtained from Maplin for less than £1.

2. Determine if it is AM or PM.

3. Select the appropriate curve for the date nearest to the current date – the inner curve is for the Summer solstice and is marked SS. (21st June in northern hemisphere). The next curve is 21st July. The third is for 21st August and the straight line is for the equinox (21st September) and marked E. The next one is for 21st October then 21st November and finally 21st of December marked WS (winter solstice). The November line is used again in January, the October line in February and so on.

TONY LYMER
GM0DHD
SPRAT 126
SPRING 2006

4. Rotate the device until the tip of the sun's shadow cast by the nail touches the appropriate curve, on the correct side of the curve, for morning or afternoon.
The 0 degree axis is now pointing to north. (Note that it is important to use the correct side of the curve for AM and PM.) .

For those not in the U.K.
The graph has been drawn for latitude 54 degrees N, but is satisfactory between about 49 and 59 degrees N, or S.

For those not in this latitude band, you can try making your own graph for the current month by using a blank piece of wood, and levelling it with, say, a bubble level, then marking the location tip of the sun's shadow over the day. The curve is a symmetrical one, and the N-S line is found by bisecting the curve using a pair of compasses. This can also be calibrated in time.

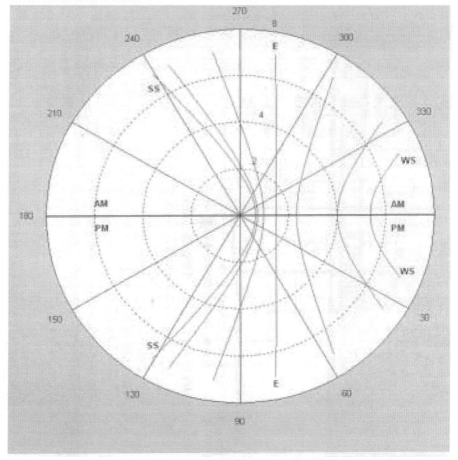

During antenna design we may need to use high voltage, anti-inductive, capacitors. But these are impossible to get in electronics shops and difficult to find in the surplus market. We can solve this problem by making capacitors from short pieces of coax cable. The capacitance between the conductor and screen braiding is some pF/cm, according to the type of cable.

For example [common cables]

RG8 = 0.95pF per cm
RG11 = 0.70pF per cm
RG58 = 0.93pF per cm
RG213 = 1.00pF per cm

So if we need a capacitor of 15pF, we can use a piece of RG213 15cm long.

But if the capacitance we require is higher, for example 50pF, it is not useful to use a piece of cable 50cm long. But we can use 5 short pieces of 10cm connected in parallel – as with normal capacitor addition.

Above - we see a capacitor example made up from 3 pieces of RG213, each 8cm long making a capacitor of 3 x 8 pF = 24pF

uH/turns on a coil

During antenna design it is useful to have some tabulation for microhenry values.

The table given here gives values for a coil of **35mm diameter**

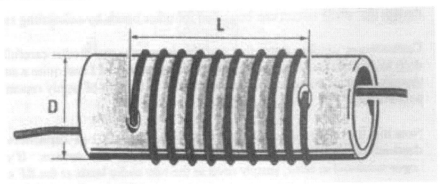

**MARCO ELEUTERI
IK0VSV
SPRAT 120
AUTUMN 2004**

Turns	Length of Coil [cm]	uH
4	12	0.5
6	18	1.0
7	20	1.5
8	25	2.0
9	38	3.0
10	38	3.5
12	40	4.0
14	40	4.5
16	45	5.0
16	50	5.5
19	55	6.0
20	58	6.5
22	62	7.0
24	65	7.5
26	68	8.0
25	70	8.5
26	70	9.0
26	76	9.5
27	80	10.0
29	80	10.5
30	85	11.0

µH/turns on a coil

Thinking to build an home made ladder line to feed a delta loop for 80 m, I have found in the article of AA1MY (SPRAT, Summer 2001 page 7) a very good solution for the construction of spreaders.

While I was planning the job I have had some additional ideas hereafter described to make easy the spreaders construction and to reduce the mechanical load on the line wires.

Material used for the spreaders.
The alternative source to the grass/weed trimmer wire mentioned in the AA1MY article has been a nylon wire used for external clothes-horse. It has a diameter of 3 mm. It is quite strong but still easy to be bent around a solder tip and rated to be weatherproof. I have bought it in an hardware store in a roll of 10 m for 7 Euros.

The bending tool (fig. 1)
To make all the spreaders with the same shape and help the bending operation I have used a refractory tile with a hole of the same diameter of the solder tip. A small piece of metal or plastic A crimped on the tile works as length reference. A "Z shaped" tool B obtained from a small stainless steel sheet helps the bending of the wire around the iron tip.

Mechanical load of the line
For the line I have used PVC insulated strand type wires.
Considering that I needed a length of about 20 m between the antenna feeding point and the tuner, I have thought that it could be better to load the weight of the line on a third insulating wire as a plastic rope.

Fig 1

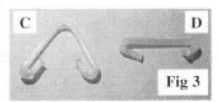

Fig 2

Fig 3

This helps to keep the line straight avoiding to pull too much the copper wires (fig. 2).
For this purpose, a "V shape" spreader C has been placed every four straight spreaders D (fig. 3).
The spreaders have been fixed with hot melting glue every 0.3 m in the way explained in AA1MY article.
A suggestion after my experience. Spreaders hooks have to be kept (cut) as short as possible and filled with the glue. This avoids that the rope gets entangled during the installation

**LUCA NORIO
IV3TEK
SPRAT 130
SPRING 2007**

QRP VERTICAL ANTENNA

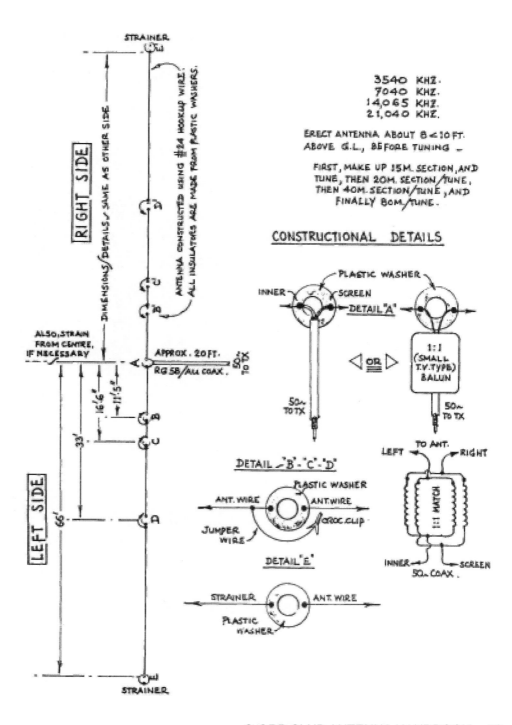

3540 KHZ.
7040 KHZ.
14,065 KHZ.
21,040 KHZ.

ERECT ANTENNA ABOUT 8 < 10 FT. ABOVE G.L., BEFORE TUNING _

FIRST, MAKE UP 15M. SECTION, AND TUNE, THEN 20M. SECTION/TUNE, THEN 40M. SECTION/TUNE, AND FINALLY 80M./TUNE.

CONSTRUCTIONAL DETAILS

PLASTIC WASHER
INNER   SCREEN
DETAIL "A"

1:1 (SMALL T.V. TYPE) BALUN

50~ TO TX

OR

50~ TO TX

DETAIL "B" - "C" - "D"
ANT. WIRE   PLASTIC WASHER   ANT. WIRE
JUMPER WIRE   CROC. CLIP

DETAIL "E"
STRAINER   ANT. WIRE
PLASTIC WASHER

TO ANT.
LEFT   RIGHT
1:1 MATCH
INNER   SCREEN
50~ COAX.

RIGHT SIDE
DIMENSIONS/DETAILS/SAME AS OTHER SIDE
ANTENNA CONSTRUCTED USING #24 HOOKUP WIRE. ALL INSULATORS ARE MADE FROM PLASTIC WASHERS.
STRAINER

ALSO, STRAIN FROM CENTRE, IF NECESSARY

APPROX. 20 FT. RG 58/AU COAX.   50~ TO TX

16'6"   11'5"

33'

66'

LEFT SIDE

STRAINER

RALPH BURCH
W8LCU
SPRAT 20
AUTUMN 1979

This is an easy way to mount a vertical or a beam on a roof. The drawings give a general idea of the construction. The idea is based on getting a plumber to make a "slate piece". This is like a large rood overflow made to suit the angle of the roof with a vertical tube of lead where the mast passes through into the roof space.

Lifting and pulling sideways can remove a tile. Fit the slate piece under the row of tiles above, on top of the tiles below and under the side tiles. The lead must give a good weatherproof overlap and therefore should be larger than the removed tile. Follow the construction data in the drawings.

If using a beam, with the rotator in the roof space, clearance is required between the lead upstand and the inside of the bottle, and between the mast and the upstand. My original leadwork cost £10.

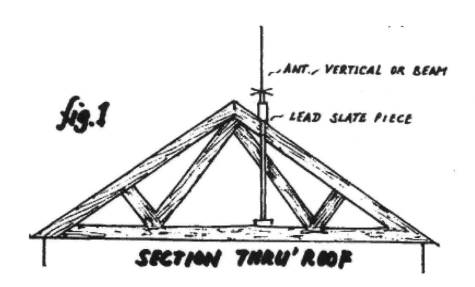

fig.1

ANT. VERTICAL OR BEAM

LEAD SLATE PIECE

SECTION THRU' ROOF

TOM SORBIE
GM3MXN
SPRAT 105
WINTER 2000/1

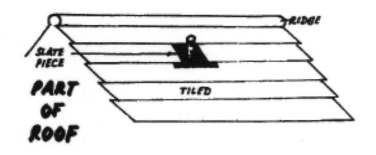

Figure 2

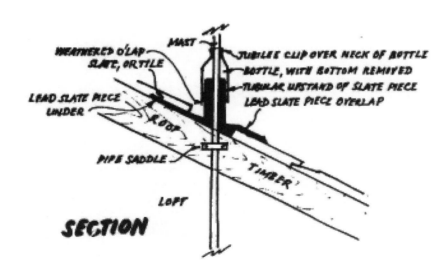

Figure 3

This mobile antenna design was the result of not having suitable materials to construct the base insulator and the loading coil of a conventional mobile antenna. Most of the material I have around the place is for fixed station beams and comprises aluminium tubing of different lengths and thicknesses.

The antenna is basically a quarter wave loaded vertical fixed directly to the metalwork of the car, without an insulator, using a suitable bracket. The prototype was fixed to the metal bumper of my old car, with two copper braid straps connecting the base of the antenna to the bodywork of the car to ensure a low resistance connection.

The break in the vertical section for the loading coil is achieved using a CB antenna base fitting mounted on a steel bracket. This bracket is fixed to the lower vertical section using a Jubilee clip (the antenna builders friend!). The loading coil is made of thick copper wire and constructed as shown in the diagram, with one end connected to the CB antenna base and the other by another Jubilee clip to the lower vertical section.

The top section was initially made from the base section of ex WD whip antenna, with a screw thread that happened to fit the CB mount. I had a problem trying to tune this assembly until Chris Page G4BUE suggested that the very top section could be made from a piece of telescoping antenna, as used in transistor radios or car antennas.

The top section now comprises a short section of WD whip antenna with the telescopic section soldered to it.

The loading coil is air spaced but uses thin strips of insulating material to make the coil structure more rigid.

The Omega match is constructed from aluminium tube with a small piece of insulating material to support the feed point and the Omega match capacitors.

I experimented with few fixed capacitors and finished up with 200pF for C1 and 150pF for C2 which gave an SWR of about 1.3:1. The top end of the Omega rod is fixed to the vertical section with yet another Jubilee clip.

This antenna is suitable for fixed station use where conventional antennas may be a problem, i.e. flat dwellers. It does require either a large metal structure (balcony railings) or a groundplane type counterpoise.

Telescopic section fine tuning adjustment

30

CB antenna mount

Jubilee clips

Loading coil 9 turns 2.75 inches diameter

45

coarse tuning adjustment

1/4inch diameter Omega match rod

2.5

41

Insulating material

Base mounting bracket

Coax feeder

All Dimensions in Inches

PETER DODD
G3LDO
SPRAT 52
AUTUMN 1987

40 METRE TOP-LOADED VERTICAL

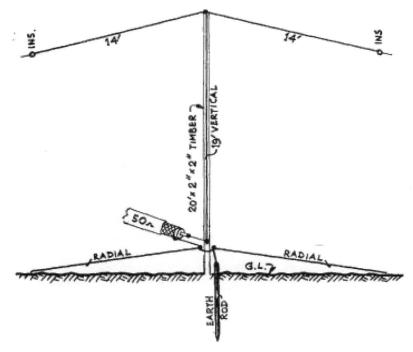

A vertical antenna can be much less than a quarter wavelength in height and still be effective if a wire top hat is used. The design given here is for about the shortest vertical section and longest top hat section that can be used without losing efficiency.

As with any vertical, an extensive radial system is required for maximum efficiency. However, I had good results with one ground rod and two 33 feet radials of vinyl covered wire laying on the surface of the ground around the house foundation. The SWR was about 1.7:1 at resonance.

The two top loading wires must be trimmed equally until resonance is obtained at different frequencies. I used a 20 feet wooden 2 x 2 inches to support the vertical on the side of the back porch. The antenna was made with size 18 wire.

BRICE ANDERSON
W9PNE
SPRAT 40
AUTUMN 1984

A TEN FOOT LONG ANTENNA COVERING SEVEN HF BANDS

This antenna has been designed as a result of many enquiries about antennas for use in restricted space areas. It is ten feet long, has a 300 ohm or open wire balanced feeder 15 feet long, and can be used on all amateur bands between between 7 and 28 MHz, erected either vertically or horizontally. It is non-critical in adjustment, all tuning being carried out with the aid of a balanced output Z-match coupler at the end of the feeder.

The antenna makes use of non-inductive end loading. This idea has been around since early this century, but was brought to the attention of the amateur fraternity by G2MQ in two RSGB "Bulletin" articles many years ago, and was also discussed by G8PG in SPRAT Number 2 back in 1975. All these articles dealt with the improvement in efficiency that could be achieved in short Marconi (monopole) antennas by using non-inductive end loading. The method was simple; to whatever length of wire that could be erected was added a further quarter wavelength of wire, wound in a series of narrow U shapes, so that its radiation cancelled out. This is shown in Fig.1. Adding this non-inductive loading to a monopole produced two important results. Firstly the current maximum appeared at the far end of the wire, out in the clear, and secondly the radiation resistance of the wire was increased, sometimes dramatically. For example at 1.8 MHz the radiation resistance of a 15 foot wire should be increased by a factor of 14, and that of a 66 foot wire by a factor of 4. Both these increases would produce significant improvements in radiated signal strength. When considering operation from a restricted size location such as an apartment block there is one great problem, however. The final efficiency of a monopole depends upon the ratio of radiation resistance to loss resistance, and the latter consists almost entirely of the resistance of the earth and/or counterpoise system which must be used with a monopole. This may often be very high (100 ohms or so) and providing a lower resistance earth in restricted locations is often impossible. In considering this problem a simple solution presented itself. If one replaced the earth connection with a second, similar loaded monopole one would have a dipole which would function without being earth connection dependent at its design frequency, and also function as a tuned doublet on all bands above that frequency and, depending on feeder length, some bands below it. As operation was now as a dipole at the design frequency a modification could be made to the amount of wire required. Each half need only now be a quarter wavelength long, with the surplus wound non-inductively.

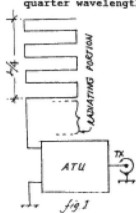

fig 1

To prove the design it was decided to construct an antenna with a design frequency of 14 MHz, and an effective radiating length of 10 feet. Two 16 ft 6 inch lengths of wire were cut, all but 5 feet of each length was folded non-inductively on suitable formers, and the free ends of the 5 foot sections were soldered to separate tags on a small tag strip which acted as centre insulator. The ends of a light weight 300 ohm feeder, 15 feet in length, were also soldered to the tags, thus completing the construction. For the experimental model a shallow cardboard box and its lid were used as formers for the two non-inductive windings, 9 holes, 1 inch apart, being punched at each end, and the surplus wire being wound in a series of narrow U shapes about 1 inch wire and 14

GUS TAYLOR
G8PG
SPRAT 64
AUTMUN 1990

inches long. Cardboard is satisfactory for indoor use, but sheets of plastic or a rectangular plastic frame would be required for outdoor use. One unexpected bonus was that the box lid was fairly loose fitting, so the radiating portion and feeder could be coiled inside the box and the lid put on when the assembly was stored! The wire used for the antenna was 7 x 0.2 mm plastic covered, which is very flexible. The feeder was light, 300 ohm plastic ribbon, although for permanent outdoor use open wire feeder spaced 2 or 3 inches would be more satisfactory. Figure 2 illustrates the set-up. Coupling the antenna to the rig is achieved by means of a Z-match with a balanced output. The basic Z-match is shown in Fig.3. The GM3OXX version appears on page 66 of the G QRP Club Circuit Handbook, and an all band version with minimum switching requirements on page 12.50 of the fifth edition of the RSGB Radio Communication Handbook. The latter version was used when testing the antenna described above.

When operating at 14 MHz and above the antenna acts as a conventional centre fed doublet. on 10 and 7 MHz it acts as a short doublet with the feeders making up the missing length. On 10 Mhz the current maximum will be about 5 feet down the feeder, and on 7 MHz at or near the bottom. Incidently do not coil up any surplus feeder length. Bring it down to the rig in gentle curves or Z shaped bends.

Tests were made with the antenna horizontal in my first floor shack (about 17ft above ground) and with it hanging vertically from the shack window. The first surprise was 7 MHz, with may good QSO's around the UK in both the horizontal and vertical modes, and other contacts well into Europe in daylight. 10 Mhz also produced daylight contacts with Europe. The hf bands produced good contacts at distances of up to around 3000 miles. The tests were made during the summer, conditions were far from outstanding and very hot weather had certainly lowered activity, so they show that despite its small size and simple construction the antenna can put out a signal. Reports were about 1 to 2 S-points down on my loop (with 180 ft of wire in it), but still quite good. The large antenna was taken down during the tests to make sure there was no re-radiation from it.

The design presented is regarded as about the smallest which will provide seven band operation. Larger versions could be made which would have higher efficiency and greater frequency coverage. Using two 33 ft wires, each with a 10 ft radiating system, and a 30 ft feeder would allow operation from 3.5 to 28 MHz. Two 66 ft wires each with a 20 ft radiating section, and a 60 ft feeder would allow operation on 1.8 to 28 MHz.
It is hoped that this article will be of assistance to those who have to operate from restricted space locations. Also that it will encourage members to experiment with the ideas outlined. Do please report your results so that we can build up more data on this type of antenna. All the tests were of course made with QRP, using 3w of CW.

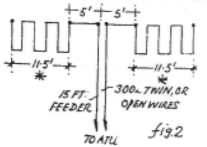

fig.2

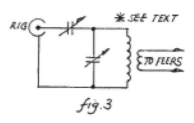

fig.3

Ever since 30 metres was opened up for general amateur use, I have been looking for an appropriate antenna for this band. I had long ago determined that vertical antennas were out of the question for my QTH because of high voltage power lines which passed within a couple of hundred feet of the property line, and their subsequent high noise levels. I needed a horizontally polarised antenna with as much man made noise rejection as possible.

The antenna about to be described appeared in the October 1983 edition of 73 Magazine by K9AZG, and therefore I cannot claim any originality for its design. However, it is one good 30 metre antenna, is cheap to build, and as it is fed from the bottom, it is horizontally polarised.

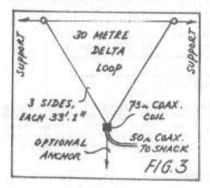

Essentially the antenna is a traditional delta loop, with the delta pointed towards the ground, and the flat top as high as possible between two supports or trees. The main difference in this delta loop is that at the bottom there is an impedance transforming system for balanced to unbalanced conversion so that the delta loop can be fed with coax and still retain a balanced radiation pattern and the highest possible efficiency.

The impedance transforming system consists of a quarter wave length of 75 ohm RG-59/U coaxial cable, wound onto a coil on a home made former, (see diagram), serving also as the feed point insulators and anchor for the feeder.

The construction details are as follows. The coil former can be made from masonite, waterproof plywood or plexiglass of quarter of an inch thick. If it is made from plywood or masonite it can be further weather proofed by spraying or brushing on a coat of polyurethane before assembly. Cut to the dimension shown in the diagram and assemble by sliding one half of the former onto the slot on the other half of the former to form an "X" shaped coil former. Then cut the quarter wave impedance matching transformer to length using the formula 234/f x 0.75. For my antenna this worked out to 234/10.125 x 0.75 = 17ft 4ins.

Weave one end of this RG-59/U into one top hole of the former and out again through the hole directly below. Leave about three inches sticking out for connections. Now close wind the coax onto the former keeping it tight.

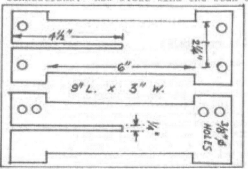

You will find that the coax just fits on the former with the dimensions shown, with enough left over for weaving through the bottom pair of holes.

The choice of the antenna wire is left to you. K9AZG used No.14 (U.S.A.) house wire, and I used No.18 copper coated steel wire. Cut the wire to length using 1005/10.125 = 99ft 3ins. Fix two insulators onto this wire, one at 33ft 1in. and the other at 66ft 2ins. These insulators allow suspending the flat top from two trees or other supports.

ED LAPPI
WD4LOO
SPRAT 47
SUMMER 1986

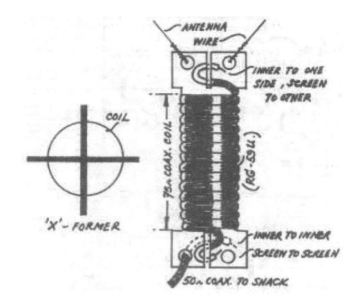

Finish your antenna by feeding the apex end wires of the delta loop into the corner holes at one end of the former. Twist each wire around itself to anchor it, strip back 3/4 inch of insulation and solder one wire to the centre conductor of the coax coil and the other wire to the shield.

Lastly, push one end of your 50 ohm feed line, (any legnth to reach the shack), into one of the corner holes at the bottom end of the coil former. Then through the other hole, pull it tight to anchor it leaving enough to make a connection. Solder the centre wire of the coil and shield to shield. Now tape or cover all the connections with sealer to weatherproof the antenna connections.

Like any other antenna, the higher the better rule applies to this one also, so raise your flat top as high as you possibly can. If you do not like the coil former swinging in the breeze, you may tie a small nylon cord to the coil former and the other end to a brick on the ground or to a stake driven into the ground.

Conclusions: As stated by K9AZG in his original article, this antenna has a SWR of 1:1 across the 30 metre band, and I am able to hear many stations that are lost in the noise when trying to use a vertical. For the money invested it has turned out to be an excellent antenna for this exciting band.

This antenna is an 8 foot square loop fed with open wire feeders and coupled to the rig via a balanced Z match similar to that used with the 10 foot long 7 band antenna described in my previous article. As with the 10 foot antenna, it was made 7 x 0.2mm insulated wire. The loop can be fed either at one corner, or at the centre of one of the 8 foot legs as shown in Fig 1. Feeder length is not critical and should be made long enough to reach the Z match. As the rig was in a corner of the shack the model described here was fed at one corner. The centre insulator can be a short length of plastic or similar material with four holes drilled in it each wire being threaded through two of them. Similar lengths of plastic can be used as feeder spreaders, with two holes bored in them. They can be secured in place with a binding of twine or thin wire around the feeder wires. When constructing the antenna cut a length of wire equal to 32 feet plus the desired length of the two feeder wires. Push a length of wire equal to the feeder length through one of the inner holes on the centre insulator, then pull the remaining wire through the corresponding outer hole, thus securing the wire. At the appropriate corner points in the loop make small securing loops, binding them in place with thin wire, then make off the free end at the centre insulator, making sure that enough wire is pulled through to provide the second leg of the feeder. Put a spacer on the feeder at each 3 foot interval and secure it with wire or twine. Suspend the assembly from suitable wall hooks by means of plastic cord, if possible allowing at least 1 foot spacing between the wires and the walls. The antenna is very light and easy to erect, support, and dismantle. Once erected one can connect the feeders to the Z match and start operations. The antenna loads with no problems on all bands 7 to 28. For the proving tests it was erected in the shack about 17 feet above ground, and horizontally. It can also be used vertically if the room height will allow this.

compared with the 10ft long antenna previously described, received signals are a little louder, because the signal capture area is larger. Performance on the hf bands from 10 MHz upwards was slightly better than the 10ft antenna, with contacts up to 4000 miles or so under summer conditions. 7 MHz provided solid inter-G working and the occasional European contact, but reports were down on the 10ft antenna. This was not unexpected, as on 7 MHz the loop is small enough to lose considerable efficiency. It still allows ragchews with Gs however.

The size is about the smallest practicable for 7 band operation. Increasing the size will increase the 7 MHz performance; a 16 foot square loop, for example, should be better on all bands 7 MHz upwards. The square shape is not essential. A length to width ratio of up to 3:1 can be used to fit the antenna into the available space. The most memorable QSO during the tests was with the U QRP Club expedition EK9QRP on 21 MHz when greetings between our two Clubs were exchanged, with 599 reports; EK9QRP was running 5W.

As with the 10 foot antenna all tests were with 3w of CW, and all other antennas were taken down.

Once again, if you experiment with this antenna or a variant of it, please report your results so that data can be collected and published.

GUS TAYLOR
G8PG
SPRAT 65
WINTER 1990/1

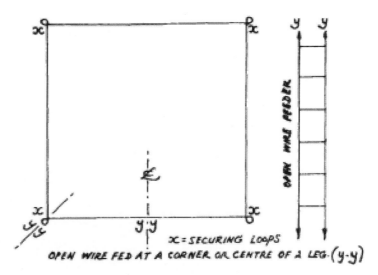

Eight foot square seven band antenna

G4VPF MOBIUS FIVE BAND LOOP

THE G4VPF MOBIUS 5 BAND LOOP.This loop makes use of the Professor Mobius theorem that any material given a twist through 180° and with its ends joined together makes an object with one side and one edge. It is constructed from a length of 300 ohm twin feeder arranged in a square as shown in Figure 1. The twist is at the opposite side from the point where the feeder is attached.Feed is via 50 ohm co-axial cable and a 4:1 balun connected "backwards", with its low impedance side to the antenna and its high impedance side to the cable. When constructed from solid dielectric 300 ohm feeder the length is found by using 1005/f x 0.8. The version shown uses 7 MHz for f, and loads well on 7, 10.1, 14, 21 and 28 MHz bands. As a precaution a suitable atu is used at the rig end of the co-ax. The velocity factor of 0.8 in the formula above is for solid dielectric 300 ohm ribbon. It may be different for slotted ribbon. (Professor Mobius was a 19th century German astronomer).

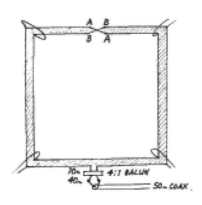

O DAVIES
G4VPF
SPRAT 84
AUTUMN 1995

Here is something which I threw together primarily for the benefit of hams living in apartments, etc., where an outside antenna is not allowed. I hope that they can use it!

Using it with five watts of RF power and sitting here in my shack (on the first floor of a frame cottage - not over ten feet above ground-level) I find it easy to work all over the USA, from coast-to-coast, and Canada. On 15 metres (cw, of course), I've also worked OK1HCH and DL1ET and hope for more DX when things improve (they've been quite poor over there lately.)

It seems to have little horizontal directivity but works much better when the plane of the loop is VERTICAL (coincident with theory for low antennas.) It might be more directive for local "Ground-wave" contacts, however. There is no doubt but what "fooling with" the dimensions, and the turns on the toroid, might improve, but this is what I found to be OK. No doubt, also, that the local electomagnetic environment will call for possible minor changes. The SWR runs between 2 and 3 on all bands specified.

It tunes to 15 metres with about 15 to 20 pF, to 20 metres with about 30 pF and to 30 metres with about 60 pF here. To use, just hook it to your rig, put a couple of watts into it and tune for greatest glow in tuning-lamp (greatest current). Then run output up to five watts and "blast away".

It seems truly marvellous to me that five watts into a little square of wire here in the shack can push a signal across four thousand miles of briny ocean, - truly, God's world is a marvellous place!

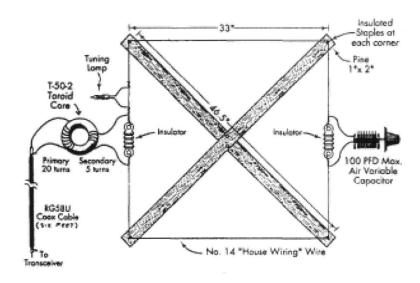

CF ROCKEY
W9SCH
SPRAT 60
AUTUMN 1989

WA3WSJ
BEAD-WIRE
ANTENNA

Subject: WA3WSJ: Bead-Wire Antenna

Date: Sun Oct 29, 2006 2:04 pm

From: Edward R. Breneiser

Hello all,

I backpack the AT here in the US and I've always wanted a small, lightweight HF antenna that won't break the bank. I finally have designed one that works great for QRP portable use.

I call it the "WA3WSJ Bead-Wire Antenna." It's made from bead wire, yes jewellery bead wire that is used to make bead jewellery! Wall Mart sells it over here packaged in a 40 foot spool. I even use the spool to store the antenna.

I take one 40' spool and tie on around 50 feet of 30lb test fishing line to one end. This is used as my radiator wire. I tie a small loop on the end of the fishing line. This loop just slips through a 1oz sinker and this is used to throw it up into a tree etc.

I also purchase two more spools and cut three 16 foot ground radials using the bead wire. I now have one 40' radiator wire and three 16' ground radial wires that I throw out around to operate. I use a BNC to two binding-post adapter that plugs into the antenna bnc on my Elecraft KX1. The whole antenna fits on one small spool and weights-in at 2oz!

Parts for the WA3WSJ Bead-Wire Antenna:

3ea. 40' bead wire spools
1 set solder less banana jacks Radio Shack # 274-721
Large spool of 30lb fishing line

So for around $10 or $11 US dollars you have a very nice compact and lightweight qrp antenna that will tune on 20m,30m and 40m. I have worked Europe with this antenna using my KX1 @ 3w on 30m.

ENJOY!

72,
Ed,WA3WSJ

EDWARD R BRENEISER
WA3WSJ
G-QRP DISCUSSION GROUP
OCTOBER 2006

J1
RCA Jack
1

18+3 / 3 turns on T50-6

Insulated connector

J2
RCA Jack
1

S1
DPDT switch

C1
180 pF

R2
47 OHM 2W

R1
47 OHM 2W

T2

R3
47 OHM 2W

D1
Red LED

20+5 turns on FT37-43

R4
470 OHM 1/4W

I built this ATU to tune my mini loaded 20m dipole (1.7m long) that I'm using in holiday with my little transceiver CW QRP MFJ CUB (2W on 20m). You must connect a low impedance antenna (near 50 Ohm) to J2 or high impedance antenna (like a half wavelength wire) to J3. The tuning range of this ATU is not so large like some other types, the resistive part of impedance of an antenna connected to J2 must be not too far from 50 Ohm, but I was able to tune many antennas connected to J2.

The SWR bridge is the classic "SVSI" by N7VE / W6JJZ / W7LS: if the led is on, there are standing waves, if the led is off, we have a low swr. T1 is made of 21 turns of 0.35mm wire on T50-6 toroid with a tap at 3 turns from ground and a link of 3 turns. 2 is made of 25 turns of 0.25mm wire on FT37-43 toroid with a 5 turns tap. he box is 53mm x 50mm x 26mm. With 50 Ohm dummy load, the losses are less than 1dB (about 0.8dB).

I never tried it but I think that this ATU must work also on 30m and 17m.

GUIDO TEDESCHI
IK2BCP/AB9DG
SPRAT 111
SUMMER 2002

This is my "mini dipole" for 20m that I built to have some fun while in holidays with my QRP setup.

It is very simple to build and you can tune it in your shack room (simulating a holiay installation in a Hotel...) using an antenna analyzer (I used my Autek VA1) but I think that you can do it also with a SWR meter and a general coverage rx/tx using low power. Start with the ends some cm longer (ex. 400 mm instead of 330 mm) and then cut both sides until you have the resonance in 20m band. Remember that the frequency is not critical because then you will "tune" the dipole with the ATU

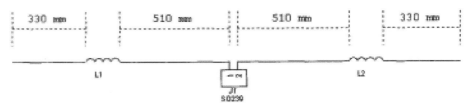

20m loaded mini dipole by ik2bcp

| 330 mm | 510 mm | 510 mm | 330 mm |

L1 = L2 = 37 turns on 61 (length) x 25 (diameter) mm form
              Wire is 0.5 mm enameled and coil is 22 mm long
J1 = SO239 connector in a little plastic box

Left – Mini-dipole centre & coils

Right – Mini-dipole in use in Irish B&B

THE G3HBN LOOP COVERING 7 TO 30 MEGAHERTZ

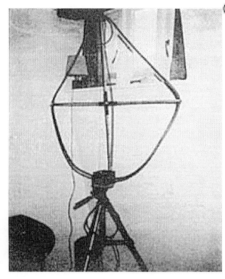

(1) Faraday link coupling between 1/5 and 1/8 diameter of main loop with braid split at centre. Adjust for 1:1 swr at 14 MHz. Use RG58U.

(2) Main loop 90 cms diameter at widest point. Needs about 4m of braid from RG213 slid over 0.5 inch plastic water hose. Final length 2.5 m including PL259 connectors.

(3) Four pieces of cane with Terry clips at ends to fit loop. Tape braid at points where clipped.

(4) Cross piece to support canes. made from 6 inch lengths of 0.5 inch plastic conduit supported by crossed Jubilee clips: used to support canes.

(5) Tuning box (plastic) containing 500+500p variable capacitor connected as split stator. PL239 sockets for loop connections and 5:1 slow motion drive. A piece of conduit pipe is fitted to the back of the box to support the vertical cane.

(6) RG58U feeder to swr meter/rig. The assembled loop is mounted on a light camera tripod. The loop conductor can be rolled up for transportation.

Used from ZB2/G3HBN/p with QRP, DX included JA, 9K2, TT8, etc etc despite very bad conditions. Over 300 QSOs were made, 36 being two-way QRP. This was with the loop on the 3rd floor balcony of a hotel. Operation from a chalet as GU/G3HBN/p in even poorer conditions produced 145 contacts with 30 European countries, 18 of them being two-way QRP.

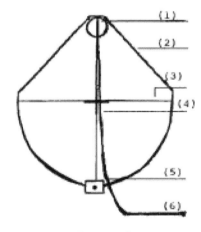

(1)
(2)
(3)
(4)
(5)
(6)

Figure 2

JR BOLTON
G3HBN
SPRAT 92
AUTUMN 1997

W9BRD COMPACT LOOP

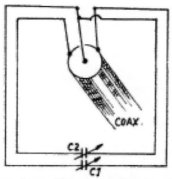

This excellent loop was developed by non-member Rod Newkirk, W9BRD, and sent to us by Rockey, W9SCH. The AAA test model was made from single, multi-strand lighting flex and the W9SCH model from 18 A.W.G. wire. The capacitors were 500 p receiving types and the feeder was a length of ancient 75 ohm TV co-ax. When assembling the loop note carefully how the two turns are connected to the co-ax: turn 1 runs from the co-ax inner via C1 to the co-ax outer, and turn 2 from the co-ax outer via C2 to the co-ax inner. The recommended size is a 5 foot square (4, ten foot lengths of wire). As the tuning range is very wide the turns must be kept taut: if they are allowed to move tuning will vary. Tuning is similar to tuning a pi coupler. Adjust one capacitor in small steps and the other through its full swing until swr drops, then make smaller adjustments to get zero swr. The AAA version of the loop covered 3.5 to 14 Mhz, so careful tuning is essential (cheap slow motion drives could help). As one would expect, only short ranges were achieved on 3.5 MHZ, but on 7 MHZ and upwards excellent results were achieved using both the AAA model and a smaller (3 FT Square) version at the W9SCH QTH. It is an excellent restricted space or /P antenna.

NOTE. Rockey, W9SCH, has produced an elegant vector analysis of how he believes this antenna works. His conclusions are that, because of the way the two loops are connected, at resonance the transmitter will feed into a reasonably high load impedance (probably resistive), that the two loops will produce a sum current considerably larger than either of their individual currents, and that the radiation will therefore be very effective.

LATE NOTE. Using his small version in a downstairs room Rockey has worked all U.S. call areas. Also, additional information from W9BRB is that if you are prepared to accept a slight swr (say 1.2;1) the loop bandwidth is very much increased.

CF ROCKEY
W9SCH
SPRAT 89
WINTER 1996/7

```
The W9SCH small version is supported by a wooden X frame.
The wire used is U.S. No 10 B & S copper, and the sides
of the outer loop are each 33 inches long. The capacitors used
are  150p. The loop tunes from  7 MHz upwards, and works
well on the higher bands. ( For serious 7 MHz work use the
bigger version described on page 26 of SPRAT No 89.) The theory
of operation is that the two loops are connected in parallel
but in phase opposition. It thus makes use of appropriate phasing
of the currents and voltages involved. For a given operating
frequency each loop is tuned a little off resonance. The two
loop currents then add vectorially, their vector resultant
then being combined at the common connecting point. Thus, when
the system is correctly tuned both the magnitude of the combined
loop-current and its phase relationship to the applied rf
are such as to reasonably match the impedance of the co-axial
feeder cable. Because the loops are of high Q neither need be
detuned enough to affect performance and the end result as an
excellent radiating system. (Note. No 10 B & s = 12 s.w.g.)
```

Subject: DDRR loops

Date: Fri Oct 27, 2006 6:04 pm

From: William Colbert

Cliff Hicks, W4MIP wrote several articles about the antenna in amateur situations.

In CQ June 1964, The DDRR antenna, a New Approach to Compact Antenna Design, and I think also in later issues of 73 magazine, It was indicated an effective antenna, especially over a ground screen. Vertically polarized and single band. Would be a great antenna in the stealth mode from the rear garden area.

One multiband installation I saw was for a mobile station – 40 thru 10 on the roof of a pick up truck camper with the larger 40 meter DDRR on the perimeter and the higher band DDRR's each within the loops. i.e. 4 DDRR antennas and each with a coaxial feed into the cab of the vehicle. Once tuned, no interaction was noted.

There was an article in QST 1972 by W2WAM and dealt with increasing the efficiency from 2 to 25%. Also, a 40 Meter DDRR by W6WYQ in QST December 1971. In the W6WYQ article, it shows details on how to electrically tune the DDRR across the band.

One footnote shows some initial articles by Boyer in Electronics Magazine January 1963 and a patent was granted to him and Northrup Corp. There was also an article by Horn in the Sept 1967 entitled The Half-wave DDRR antenna. And in the 46th issue (1969)of the ARRL Handbook.

WILLIAM COLBERT
W5XE
G-QRP DISCUSSION GROUP
OCTOBER 2006

THE G2WI MULTI-BAND VERTICAL

I made this one from information supplied by G2WI.
Operated over a good ground system it gave very good
results. When correctly tuned it operates as a
$\frac{1}{4}$ wave on 40 metres, $\frac{1}{4}$ wave on 15 m, $\frac{1}{2}$ wave on 20 m,
and $\frac{3}{4}$ wave on 10m. Although not tried, it should be
possible to add additional stubs for the WARC bands.
In my version a $1\frac{1}{2}$ inch diameter metal mast was used
for the 33ft 9 inch section. If a non-metalic mast is
to be used, 4 wires 33ft 9 inches long and soldered
together at their ends can be used to simulate the
metal mast (this is to provide a broad band section).
The stubs are spaced 3 inches from the mast, being
attached to lengths of glass fibre pcb which have
aluminium angle brackets attached to them. These
are clamped to the mast with Jubilee clips which can
also be used to connect the bare ends of the stubs
to the mast. Carefully weatherproof these connections
and all other connections used in the system.Use
heavy guage wire for the stubs, terminate them on
insulators and fit turnbuckles for tensioning.

Setting up is as follows. Check the 33ft 9 inch
section for 1:1 swr at 7050 KHz ; adjust length if
necessary. Do this with the stubs disconnected.
Attach the 16ft 9 inch stub; trim its length for
minimum swr (about 1.2:1 at 14,200 KHz).Add the
8ft 6 inch section and carefully trim for lowest swr
at 28,550 KHz. Check swr at 21.25 MHz ; it should be
about 1.1:1. If radial lengths for the different bands
are used disconnect any earth connection and trim
them individually for lowest swr on the band.Elevated
radials should work well.

JACK HOLSTEAD
G3OZC
SPRAT 91
SUMMER 1997

The last two issues of SPRAT have both contained methods of voltage feeding a half wave antenna; this is yet a third method. It does not need a counterpoise and can feed any wire that is one or more half wavelengths long. Figure 1 shows the circuit arrangement. For 15 metres C1 and C2 are each 47 pF and L is 14 turns of 18 swg wire, spaced over 45mm on a 25mm diameter former. For 20 metres C1 and C2 are each 56 pF and L is 19 turns of 18 swg wire spaced over 45mm on a 25 cm diameter former. For 40 metres C1 and C2 are each 82 pF and L is 32 turns of 18 swg wire spaced over 45 mm on a 25 mm diameter former. The LC combination is in series resonance from the rig and parallel resonance with the antenna, so a high voltage is developed across the capacitors. My design used 500V working capacitors because they were available. A length of RG8 co-ax (1pF per cm) could be used to make a single high voltage capacitor. To tune, expand or compress the turns of L to obtain the lowest swr which should be less than 1.2:1. If it is not the antenna is not in resonance and its length should be adjusted until the required swr can be obtained. For other bands scale the capacitor value then wind a coil to give resonance, as the LC value is important. The 500V working capacitors are suitable for QRP. A QRO version for 20m using 4 KV working capacitors worked well also.

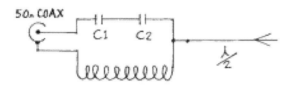

Figure 1

HOW ABOUT CURRENT FEED THEN ??

Illustration from the 1933 Edition of the ARRL Handbook
Text by SPRAT Technical staff.

Figure 2 shows some simple methods of current feeding an antenna at the ATU. What we do is to break the antenna at a point of reasonably low impedance, insert the ATU at that point and use the remainder of the antenna wire as a counterpoise. Provided we move far enough from the end of the antenna but not too far we will get a nice feed impedance and little effect on the radiating efficiency of the wire. If we have a half wavelength of wire feeding between half and three quarters the distance from the centre to one end will give us feed point impedances of around 70

MA EALES
M0AJL
SPRAT 97
WINTER 1998/9

to 300 ohms, easily handled by the atu. The counterpoise can be run at an angle to the main wire and inside the house if necessary, so that may help on cramped sites. Fig 2 shows parallel tuned circuits for the coupler as used in 1933. Today a Z-match or L-network should be used, with the counterpoise section of the wire connected to its ground terminal. NOTE. The 1933 handbook belonged originally to W1FSK who bequeathed it to Al, K8lFK. Al, who is terminally ill, has now given the book to G8PG. W1FSK was Al's uncle.)

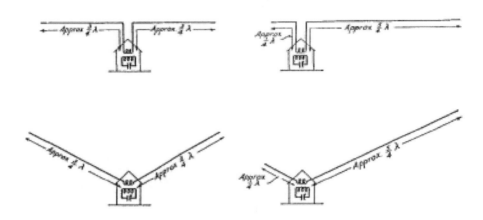

END FEEDING A HALF-WAVE WIRE

A METHOD OF END FEEDING A HALF WAVE WIRE VIA A CO-AX CABLE has been drawn to our attention by Lutz, DL2HRP. It is shown below.

This is the 14MHz version, and it can be scaled for other bands. Lutz erected his by twisting the wire around a 9m plastic fishing pole. Lutz found the idea in "Antennenbuch" by DM2ABK. (Presumably published in DDR days). Take care to thoroughly weatherproof all joints and cable ends.

**LUTZ BERGNER
DL2HRP
SPRAT 81
WINTER 1994/5**

There seems to have been a lot of interest lately in the use of kites in amateur radio. Here's a home made design that'll support a topband quarter wave (if not more), will fly in quite a moderate breeze doesn't need helium and won't cost you £210 (+ postage)! It's not a particularly original design, but it WILL work

You'll need:
1. A sheet of tough polythene 36 x 38", such as a garden refuse bag (an ordinary bin liner probably won't be tough enough)
2. Two pieces of quarter inch wood dowel 36" long
3. Two "cover buttons" (from haberdashers shops)
4. PVC or masking taps, string etc

First step is to cut out the sheet according to fig 1. Polythene can be a bit tricky to cut straight - you need some good sharp scissors, or better still, some dressmaker's electric scissors. Take particular care over the holes. Then use tape to attach the two dowels as in fig. 2.

The next step is to use plenty of tape to strengthen the corners where the cord will be attached. Use a layer on both sides of the plastic, then make a small hole and attach the cover buttons (fig 3). The loop on the buttons should be on the same side as the dowels, i.e. facing towards you as the kite is flown.

Finally, cut a piece of cord about six feet long, tie a loop in the centre (where the line will be attached), tie the ends to the loops on the cover buttons, and your Mega-Kite is ready for flight!

The line needs to be lightweight but strong. I use the bright orange "string" from hardware stores, although you could buy proper kite line from a good toy shop. Remember, it's the line, NOT the wire that takes the strain - if you just attach a piece of wire to the kite it'll just stretch and snap. The wire needs to be thin and multi-stranded (e.g. Maplin's 7/0.2), since single-core will probably break /

There's umpteen arrangements of kits and aerial that will put out a good signal, so I'll leave that side of things up to you. I use a 40m wire as a halfwave on 80m and a quarter wave on topband. A counterpoise wire running along the ground can also be added, especially if the ground is dry.

One warning. Obviously, you won't be suicidal enough to go kiting in a thunderstorm a la Ben Franklin. However, even on a sunny day the wind blowing can generate enough static to damage solid-stage front ends. It's essential that this can discharge to an earth spike. Either use an ATU that is DC short to earth, or else allow the static to discharge through a high-ish value resistor (e.g. 22k that won't absorb too much RF).

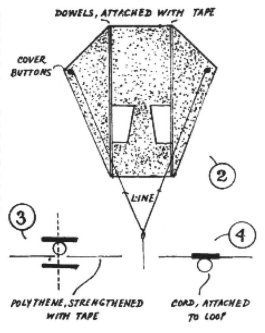

DOWELS, ATTACHED WITH TAPE

COVER BUTTONS

LINE

③ POLYTHENE, STRENGTHENED WITH TAPE

④ CORD, ATTACHED TO LOOP

MARK PALMER
G0OIW
SPRAT 84
AUTUMN 1995

If, like me you're used to a grotty sort antenna in an area of high time-base QRM, you'll find working /P in the countryside with the Pythagoras Mega-Kite a total delight. Good luck!

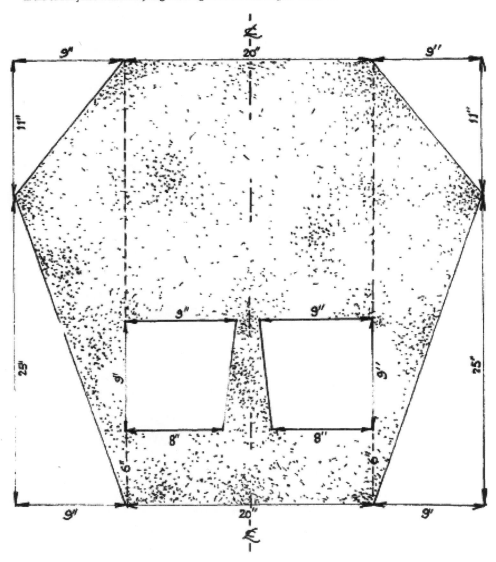

This antenna originated from DARC QRV Magazine December 1971, and should be attributed to DJ2KT. It is the FD-4 and it is all it is claimed of it.
The match on 4 band has a low SWR on 80, 40, 20, 10m and can match without an ATU and is claimed to out-perform the other multi band ants.
It is based on the "Windom" principle in that the feed pointon 80, 40, 20, 10m all coincide one third from one end of a 42m long antenna. It could be matched with 300 ohm ribbon at that point.
However DJ2KY matches witha balun 4:1 for 75   6:1 for 50
Step up unbalanced coax to balanced antenna.

I have found it works exactly as stated and is a good antenna, unfortunately it does not match on 21MHz.
At far as the WARC bands are concerned 10MHz is a poor match but 18MHz, 24MHz are acceptable. I have used an ATU on 21 and 10.1MHz with good reports.
If QRO is put into a mismatched balun it will heat up. "So stick to QRP".

A balun is easy to make (4 to 1) as in Rad Comm G6XN, December 1989, Page 57 made from scrap ferrite rod.
I used twin coloured wire grey and black wound together six turns.
Coax screen to join of black and grey coax inner to either black or grey which is connected to one side of antenna I have taped the balun to a large insulator. My antenna is bent down at one end.

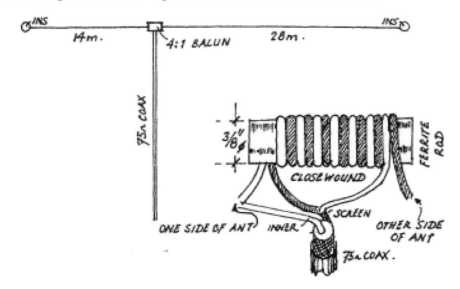

TOM SORBIE
GM3MXN
SPRAT 64
AUTUMN 1990

G3ZOF PORTABLE WHIP ANTENNA

This mobile whip was built by G3ZOF using the top section of a glass fibre fis hing rod. The whole coil tunes 7m Hz the tap is for 14mHz on 21 a metal bush replaces the coil. The feeder length is critical.

With an HW7 and the whip mounted atop of a Viva Van, G3ZOF has had CW reports in the 3 4 to 8 range from most of Europe on 14 and 21. Results have not yet been obtained on 7mHz because of band condx when the unit was used, but it does load on the band.

~0.5cm

GLASS FIBRE WHIP 131cm LONG HELICAL WOUND 16swg ALUMINIUM WIRE

[ALL WINDINGS CLOCKWISE FROM BASE]

SCREW WHIP

BASE LOADING COIL

19 TURNS

6cm

45 Turns 18 swg

12 cm

SHORTING LINK FOR 14MHz. [7MHz. FULL COIL]

1-2cm.

METAL BUSH TO REPLACE COIL ON 21 MHz

6cm

NOTE
TOTAL LENGTH OF ALUMIN. WIRE = 146cm on whip.
LENGTH OF COAX FROM RIG TO BASE MOUNTING [Critical] = 366 cm

GQ WHEELER
G3ZOF
SPRAT 17
WINTER 1978/9

THE G3WQW MINI DOUBLET

Based on an antenna described in SPRAT No.64, this version should be fed via an atu having a balanced output. The end loading coil formers are made from 3 inch square pieces of suitable thickness outdoor grade plywood, well varnished. Each piece has 8 holes drilled equidistantly into it to take the wire, and also a larger, 22 mm diameter hole in its centre which has one end of a 16½ inch length of white electrical conduit (plastic pf course) cemented into it to act as a spacer. Each end piece also has a hook attached to it to allow a piece of thin cord to be attached to it for tensioning the whole assembly. It should be possible to load the antenna on all hf bands, but its best performance is likely to be from 10 MHz upwards.

F SIMS
G3WQW
SPRAT 89
WINTER 1996/7

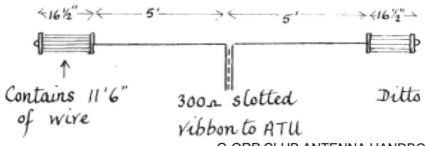

←16½"→ ←   5'   → ←   5'   → ←16½"→

Contains 11'6" of wire

300Ω slotted ribbon to ATU

Ditto

This antenna consists of a loaded wire approximately 7m long,
which is worked against a ground rod, two 10m radials , and one
7m radial. The antenna is normally sloped at an angle of 45°.
With this slope there will be 3dB of gain in the direction

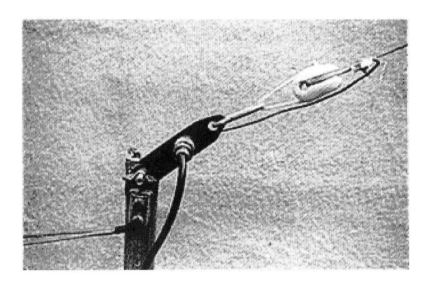

of the radials, which are set out facing away from the low end of
the antenna. On 14 and 3.5 MHZ the radials can be adjusted to
give an swr not exceeding 2.1:1; this can be reduced to 1:1 with
a sutable atu. Using such an atu it is also possible to load the
antenna on on 18,10 and 7 MHZ with an acceptable swr.The design
described is suitable for powers up to 100 W. Bandwidth is about
50 kHz on 3.5 MHZ and 100 kHz on 14 MHZ. The antenna consists of
a 4.55m length of 13/0.109 BWG insulated wire, a coil consisting
of 70 turns of 0.5mm (25/0.020 BWG) enamelled wire wound on a
40 x 150 mm plastic former, then a further 2.3m of the antenna wire.
These items are shown in the photo on our front cover. Insulators

MAX O ALTMANN
DL7RU
SPRAT 85
WINTER 1995/6

insulators are fitted to the free ends of the antenna, a tail beig
left at the end of the 4.55m section to allow connection to the
co-axial socket. This socket is mounted on a piece of copper
sheet 100x25x3mm. A hole at one end of this piece of copper
allows the cord from the lower antenna insulator to be fastened
to it via a quick release hook. The co-axial socket is fitted
in a hole drilled in the piece of copper at its centre, and a
hole at the other end allows piece of copper to be firmly bolted
to the top of a 1.2m galvanised ground spike . The ends of the
three radials, which are made from the same wire type as the antenna,
are soldered together, then firmly bolted to the earth spike
immediately below the point where the copper plate is attached.
As already stated, two 10m and one 7m radials are used. When
erecting the antenna drive the ground rod into the ground until
it is far enough in to keep the radials 0.6m above ground (see
photo 2). The far end of each radial is terminated on an insulator
which is connected to a peg long enough to keep the radial 0.6m
above ground. The 7m radial is erected in line with the antenna,
and the others on each side of it at 45° to the run of the
antenna. The radial lengths may need trimming for best swr;
it should be possible to make fine adjustments by slightly
altering the height above ground of one or more radials.For
a permanent installation weatherproofing is important. The
co-axial connector can be weatherproofed by embedding it in
"Plasticine" (R) modelling clay; the coil should be thoroughly
weatherproofed with a suitable insulating material. After
soldering the copper plate should be laquered and and the
connections to the ground stake should be painted over.This
antenna has been erected and used in various exotic African and
Asian locations over the years, and has always given good results.
At a fixed location with enough space it should be possible to
increase efficiency by using more radials. I have also used
it "upside down" with the radials on a roof and the antenna
pointing downwards. It worked very well !

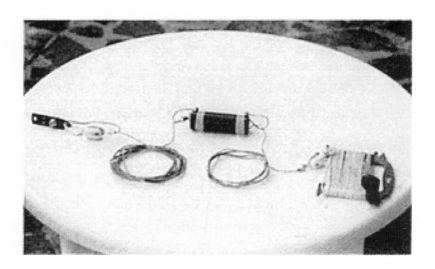

I was very interested to hear of John McDonnell's (G3DOP) experiments with the Hula Hoop antenna. I have been using a similar antenna for mobile use for the last ten months and the following is a description of its construction and results.

My antenna is based on the DDRR antenna described in the ARRL antenna handbook. The design data is reproduced below.

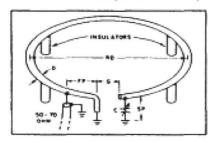

RD = 0.078 λ (28")
SP = 0.11D (2.5")
FP = 0.25 h (See Note 1)
C = (See Note 2)
D = (See Note 3)
G = (See Table 4)

Feet X 0.3048 = m.

Inches X 25.4 = mm.

Notes: (1) Actual dimension must be found experimentally. (2) Value to resonate the antenna to the operating freq. (3) d ranges upward from 1/2" (13 mm). The larger "d" is the higher efficiency is. Use largest practical size. e.g., 1/2" (13 mm) for 10 meters, 5" (127 mm) or 6" (152 mm) for 80 or 160 meters.

Band (Meters)	160	80	40	20	15	10	6	2
Feed Point (FP)	12"	6"	6"	2"	1.5"	3"	1"	1/2"
Gap (G)	18"	7"	5"	3"	2.5"	2"	1.5"	1"
Capacitor, pF (C)	150	100	70	35	15	15	10	5
Spacing (Height) (SP)	48"	24"	11"	6"	4 3/4"	3"	1 1/2"	1"
Tubing Diameter (D)	5"	4"	2"	1"	3/4"	3/4"	1/2"	1/4"
Ring Diameter (RD)	36'	18'	9'	4.5'	3'4"	2'4"	16 1/4"	6"

Figure 1 DDRR Antenna (from ARRL Antenna Handbook)

My version of the DDRR antenna was constructed out of copper tubing because of the availablity of plumbing material. The antenna was given a square configuration because I didnt have tube bending equipment necessary to make the circular configuration called for in the design. I also reasoned a square would look like a roof rack and be less obtrusive, although I did'nt know if it would work. The design used 90 degree joints, used in plumbing, for the corners.

I made two variants; the first was made as close to the original DDRR design as possible because I did'nt know how it worked. The rather imposing title of Directional Discontinuity Ring Radiator made me think it was some sort of slot antenna.

The average height of the element was 6 inches above ground (in this case the roof of the car) although the overall element length was more because of the problem of the capacitor. A conventional tuning capacitor was not used because it was not available; making a capacity tuning unit that would be weatherproof at 70MPH was a bit beyond my constructional capabilities. A capacitor was constructed by fixing a plastic block near to the 'top' end of the element, which held the element a fixed distance away from the roof of the car. By moving the block along the element against the curved surface of the roof enabled the roof/element distance, and the capacitance, to be varied.

This antenna appeared to perform well using 10 watts output but only two transatlantic QSOs were made during three months of intermittent use. I decided to modify the design after reading a mathematical analysis of this antenna by Robert Dome, W2WAM (QST July 1972). This analysis gave the original QST DDRR antenna an efficiency of 2.75%, mainly because the low radiation resistance caused the conductor ohmic losses to consume much of the available power. He suggested that by increasing the height to 20 inches (for 20 metres) and using good coductivity materials the efficiency could be raised to 25.8%, an increase of 9.8db signal strength.

PETER DODD
G3LDO
SPRAT 51
SUMMER 1987

I regarded a roofrack 20 inches above the roof of the car a bit obtrusive so the design in Figure 2 represents a compromise, with an average height of 10 inches above the roof of the car. It is fixed to the car by genuine bar roof rack, the sort used to transport ladders etc. The bars are set about 12 inches apart and a sheet of aluminium attached to the bars. When this is done the clamp nearest where the vertical section of the element is to go is removed.

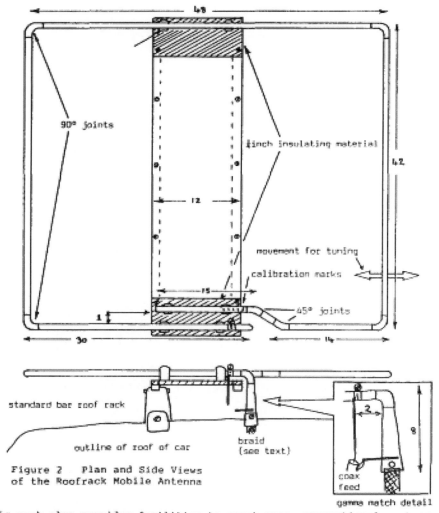

all dimensions in inches

Figure 2   Plan and Side Views of the Roofrack Mobile Antenna

This rack also provides facilities to mount more conventional antennas for comparative tests.
Two pieces of bakerlite or paxolin are fitted to the ends of the rack for mounting the element. The element is made of 22mm copper tubing, similar to the Mk1, and fixed to the insulating sections with plastic 22mm tube to wall fixings, providing double insulation.

It is tuned by the capacitance of the overlapping element end along the base of the element. This overlap, and hence the capacitance, is varied by moving the front part of the element as shown by the arrows; the top of the element slides in the plastic tube clamps.

The base of the element is flattened so that it will sit in the roof gutter and is attached like a roof rack using part of the removed vertical clamp. Additional electrical contact is provided by braiding, soldered to the base of the element, and attached to the door post with self tapping screws; this is done at a point covered when the door is closed.

A thick piece of wire is also soldered to the base of the element so that the braid of the coax can be soldered to it when the antenna is installed. The centre of the coax feed is fixed to the element by a jubilee clip so that it can be adjusted for the correct feedpoint.

The antenna can be matched using the lowest SWR although it is better first to resonate the element using a GDO. I measured the actual impedance as described in SPRAT 50 and this is shown in Figure 3.

The transatlantic QSO count, using 10 watts, has now gone up dramatically to about two QSOs per week operating half an hour in the middle of the day during week days. The antenna does produce a bit of wind noise at 70MPH but on the other hand its unobtrusive disguise as a roof rack does have some advantages.

Freq	Input Parameters				RESULTS		+/- Errors	
	A	C	D	E	Res	jX	Res	jX
14.11	158	130	70	75	50.7	-52.3	12.8	12.4
14.12	150	125	70	67	50.3	-42.2	6.8	7.2
14.13	143	114	71	61	52.7	-29.1	3.2	3.3
14.14	135	101	70	59	56.9	-12.9	1.7	1.8
14.15	131	92	70	63	62.6	+2.8	0.6	0.8
14.16	131	87	71	75	71.4	+21.6	0.5	1
14.17	131	84	70	89	77.7	+39.4	1.6	5.1
14.18	141	92	71	113	90.7	+60.4	1.5	12.1
14.19	159	110	72	141	107.7	+93	0.9	5.3

Figure 3 Impedance Plot (via 0.15 wavelengths of coax)

LESSER-KNOWN AERIALS: THE W3EDP

Developed by W3EDP around 1936, this aerial was very popular before the last war. It still has its adherents, and in post-war years it has provided outstanding QRP contacts for some of the stations using it. The system consists of an aerial 84 feet long, parallel tuned against counterpoises, except on 1.8 MHz where it is tuned against ground if possible (although the 17 ft counterpoise can be used with some loss of efficiency). For all other bands except 14 MHz the aerial is tuned against a 17 foot long counterpoise, and on 14 MHz a separate 6½ foot long counterpoise is employed. The counterpoises must be well insulated and kept clear of walls etc. If possible they should be erected at rightangles to the aerial. Fig 1 shows the arrangement, including an aerial coupling unit suitable for use with modern, low impedance output transmitters. In this coupler C2/L1 must resonate at the operating frequency. Coil L2 should be close wound over L1, using two thirds the number of turns in L1. The value of C1 will vary between around 900 pF for 1.8 MHz to around 50 pF for 28 MHz. If an all band coupler is required a twin gang 500 pF variable capacitor with the two sections in parallel can be used for C1. C1 is used to match the system, and C2 is used to tune it to resonance, the tuning procedure being similar to that used with the pi tank output circuit.

FIG.1.

TO TX   C2   C1   L1   L2   14MHz   17ft.   6½ft.

GUS TAYLOR
G8PG
SPRAT 17
WINTER 1978/9

TWO DIPOLE COLINEAR

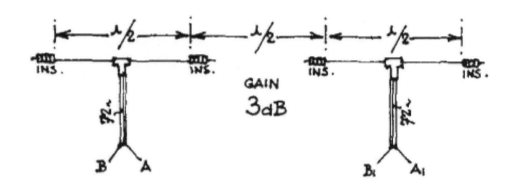

GAIN
3dB

BRIAN BOOTH
G3SYC
SPRAT 30
SPRING 1982

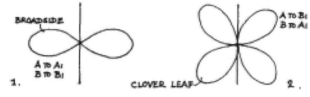

1. In phase broadside, connect A to A' and B to B'

2. Out of phase cloverleaf, connect A to B' and B to A'

BROADSIDE

A to A₁
B to B₁

1.

CLOVER LEAF

A to B₁
B to A₁

2.

The gain is about 3dBs

One must use an ATU connected to the junction of the feeders, to take care of the 36 ohm feed.

It is a very good antenna and should suit the single band man.

A MUCH IMPROVED VERSION OF THE G5RV ANTENNA

28·5 m.

400 ~   13·5 m.

50 ~ ANY   LENGTH
TO RIG

BRIAN AUSTIN
G0GSF
SPRAT 120
AUTUMN 2004

This antenna is the result of research carried out in the 1980s at the UniversityW of Wiitwatersrand. The object was to modify the G5RV to improve its effectiveness by reducing the swr on as many bands as possible. The final version is shown in Fig.1. With this configuration its is possible to use the antenna on the 7, 14, 18 and 24 MHz bands with the co-ax feeder connected directly to the rig and no ATU in circuit. The remaining bands in the range 3.5 to 28 MHz can be used with the aid of an ATU. The design offers good efficiency and performance when compared with the original G5RV. The whole project and its background are described in detail on pages 167 to 173 of the I.E.R.E. Journal for August 1987. Copies can be obtained from G8PG but do please send an adequate amount tocover copying and postage costs.

This antenna is compact and easy to construct. A 28 MHz model has been on trial for about six months and appears to have the same gain as a Quad. The front-to-back ratio is about five S points according to local reports, and this and the gain correlates well with the data obtained from a VHF model.

Other data obtained from the VHF model indicates that the 14, 21 and 28 MHz versions may be interlaced without detuning but the feed impedance is disturbed. This means that separate feed line and Gamma matching is required for each driven element. Further data will be made available when the necessary tests are complete.

The light weight and low windage of the Double D enabled me to me to put the 28 MHz model up to 45 feet (13 metres) on a thin unguyed mast. Using this antenna with a QRP 3 watt output SSB homemade transceiver I worked all continents in 5 days and 24 American states in 3 months.

Design Data

Freq MHz	Reflector		Driv: Elt:		A		B		C		D	
	in	cm	in	cm	in	cm	in	cm	in	cm	in	cm
14.2	452	1147	417	1060	245	622	263	668	180	457	33	84
21.25	302	767	279	708	154	390	166	420	113	287	22	56
28.5	225	572	208	528	114	290	122	310	85	216	15	38

The above figures are based on the formula below

Driven Element.
$$\frac{5920}{f} = L \text{ inches.} \qquad \frac{15050}{f} = L \text{ (cm)}$$

Reflector
$$\frac{6413}{f} = L \text{ inches.} \qquad \frac{16288}{f} = L \text{ (cm)}$$

1. The above formula for PVC wire only, Multiply L by 1.04 if using uninsulated copper wire

2. See figs 2 and 3 for meaning of A,B,C and D dimensions.

3. Figures in C only approximate and are an aid to construction

4. A,B,C,and D not critical and need not be altered if the elements are tuned to the band edge.

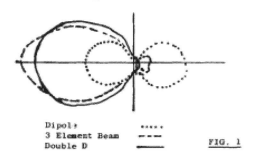

Dipole ·····
3 Element Beam – – –
Double D ——————   FIG. 1

HORIZONTAL POLAR DIAGRAM COMPARISONS USING 145.6 MHz MODELS

PETER DODD
G3LDO
SPRAT 23
SUMMER 1980

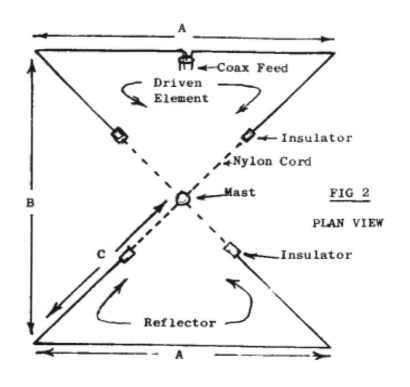

Coax Feed

Driven Element

Insulator

Nylon Cord

Mast

FIG 2

PLAN VIEW

Insulator

Reflector

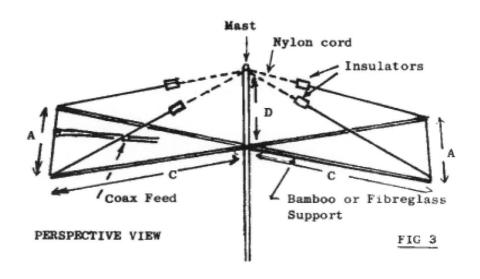

Mast

Nylon cord

Insulators

Coax Feed

Bamboo or Fibreglass Support

PERSPECTIVE VIEW

FIG 3

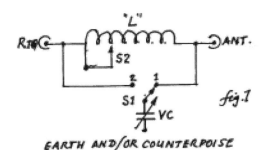

EARTH AND/OR COUNTERPOISE

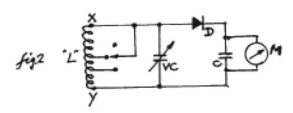

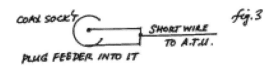

Many beginners on h.f. begin by using a dipole. There is nothing wrong with this and a dipole can give good results, but it is by nature a single band antenna. So for most of us multi-band hf work will involve the use of an end-fed antenna. To use such an antenna one will need an antenna tuning unit (atu) and either an s.w.r. indicator or a multi-band r.f. indicator. A simple a.t.u. is the L-network shown in Fig 1. With S1 in position 1 it will match impedances higher than the TX output impedance, and with the switch in position 2 it will match impedances lower than the TX output impedance. The switch S2 allows the correct value of inductance for the band in use to be selected. L1 is wound on a 3cm diameter former using 40 turns of 24 s.w.g. or similar enamelled copper wire. Taps are made at 2 turns, 4 turns, then each further 4 turns. The variable capacitor should be 200p or larger. With these values the unit should cover all bands 7 MHz to 30 Mhz. Many rigs have a built-in swr meter and an excellent circuit for one appears on page 12 of the G QRP C "Antenna Handbook". A suitable circuit for

AAA TECHNICAL STAFF
SPRAT 104
AUTUMN 2000

a tunable r.f. indicator is shown in Fig.2. L can be wound on a 3 cm diameter former,using 30 turns of 24 s.w.g. or similar wire. The coil is tapped at 4 turns and 12 turns. CV can be 150p or larger and C 1000p or larger (not critical). D is any small signal diode, and M an analogue meter reading 0-1 mA or less. If no calibration source such as a g.d.o. is available sufficiently accurate calibration for each band can be achieved by connecting point y on Fig 2 to the antenna terminal of a receiver via a short lead, and connecting a metre or so of wire to point X on the diagram. The receiver is then tuned to a strong signal on the desired band and S1 and CV are used to tune across each range of the indicator until a point is found where the strength of the incoming signal is reduced to a minimum. The r.f. indicator is then tuned to the band the receiver is tuned to. The connections to X and Y are then removed once the desired bands have been calibrated.

Let us now turn our attention to how one tunes up a long wire antenna. If one already has a dipole with a feeder 7m or more in length or a v.h.f. beam with a similar length of feeder, one has a ready made long wire to experiment with. Make up the simple adaptor shown in Fig.3 and use it to connect the shack end of the co-ax feeder to the rig via the L-network. You then have a top loaded long wire antenna. To adjust the L-network to approximate resonance on the desired band tune the receiver to this band then try each position of S2 in turn until one is found where rotating CV peaks the received signal to a maximum. Make final fine adjustments by either (a) tuning CV for minimum reading on the s.w.r. meter (if available) or (b) tuning the r.f. indicator to the desired band, placing its coil close to the co-ax being used as an antenna and adjusting CV on the L-network for maximum reading on the r.f. indicator meter. If it is impossible to get correct tuning on a particular band first try temporarily connecting a metre or so of wire in series with the co-ax being used as the antenna. If this provides no improvement switch S1 on the L-network to position 2 and repeat the tuning procedure.

While using the feeder of a dipole or vhf beam as an end fed antenna is an excellent way of learning the tuning procedures (and may give surprising results) ,the serious h.f. operator will soon want a proper multi-band end fed wire. Whereas with a dipole we take pains to make the wire resonant, this is not a good idea with a multi-band end fed antenna, as it will give a very high feed point impedance on one or more bands . It may be possible to overcome this problem by slightly lengthening or shortening the wire, but it is best to avoid it altogether. Avoidance has been complicated by the W.A.R.C. bands, which are not harmonically related, but for the bands from 7 Mhz to 30 MHz tests using the coupler shown in Fig 1 indicate that a length of 75 feet (23m) can be loaded with no problems (adding 20 turns to L in the coupler should also allow 3.5 MHz operation). It will increase efficiency if one or two counterpoise wires – say 33 feet, 16 feet and 11 feet are connected to the ground terminal on the coupler. They can be run indoors or outdoors. Get the antenna as high as possible. If you are short of space do not be afraid to bend it a bit and/or run part of it in your roof space. Knowing how to handle a long wire antenna means you can operate almost anywhere. We hope this has taken most of the mystery out of it.

The bungalow I live in has very restricted antenna space, so I am constantly playing with small antennas. The two about to be desribed have worked well for me, and should be of use to other members with little antenna space. The first, shown in Fig 1, is a two radial ground plane , the vertical element of which is made from a slinky. It is co-ax fed, with a ferrite clamp attached to the to the cable neaar the feed point. It can be used on both 24 and 28 mhz. The slinky used is of 37.5 mm diameter and enough of the top turns are tied together to to bring the antenna into resonance on 28 to 29 MHz. I use frequencies in the range 28060 to 29600 KHz and find the antenna pretty broad band, but a suitable atu will provide maximum efficiency. By altering the number of turns tied together at the top of the antenna section it can also be tuned to 24 MHz. The radials are each a quarter wave of wire cut for 28 or 24 MHz, but if roof space is limited slinkies could be used. Note that slinkies of 69.5 mm diameter are also available, thus providing interesting possibilities for small lower band antennas.

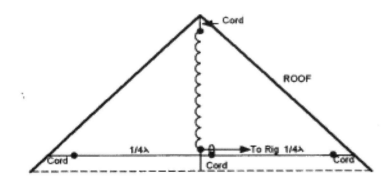

FIG.1.

EDDIE MCLEAN
GM4EWM
SPRAT 125
WINTER 2005/6

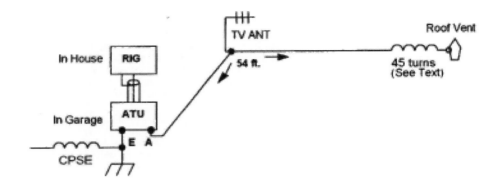

FIG.2.

The second antenna, Fig 2, is a loaded lower band antenna fed via a fairly long length of co-ax cable the remote end of which terminates at an L-match tuner which in turn feeds the antenna. This tuner is earthed both to a ground connection and to a counterpoise consisting of 66 feet of wire helically wound on a plastic pipe former. The antenna consists of 54 feet of wire with a loading coil at the far end. This coil consist of 45 feet of wire wound on a 2.75 inch diamete plastic pipe. To reduce inductance the first half the the turns are wound clockwise and the second half anti-clockwise. In my installatin the final shape is that of a normal antenna laid on its side, but Fig 2 has been drawn to show the essential ideas so the they can be adapted for use in other restricted area layouts. The use of an automatic atu would also be a possibility in many instanes and could be money well spent

MORE ON THE DOUBLE D BEAM

In the Summer 1980 edition of SPRAT I wrote an article on the Double-D antenna. I subsequently received letters from readers expressing disappointment in the performance of this antenna. I recently moved QTH and constructed a 21 Mhz version from my own formula and the results were also disappointing.

Since then much experimental work has been done and the following data is the result of this. The drawings also give some construction tips.

From the graph below the feed impedance is rather low at resonance. If the SWR of nearly 2:1 bothers you, extend the length of the driven element by about 2% and neutralise the reactance with a capacitor of an Xc of 100 - 125 ohms. Typically, at 21 Mhz, an extension of 2 inches (5cm) each side - 4 inches in total (10cm) - of the driven element and a shunt capacitor of 60-70 pf

The polar diagram was obtained from the S meter of a transceiver while rotating the antenna. A suitable modulated signal was generated by a signal generator located in the apex of the roof of the house, at nearly the same height as the antenna and at a distance of three wavelengths.

DIMENSION	INCHES	CM
A and B	$\frac{3350}{f}$	$\frac{8516}{f}$
C	$\frac{2370}{f}$	$\frac{6025}{f}$
E	$\frac{1336}{f}$	$\frac{3397}{f}$
D	$\frac{700}{f}$	$\frac{1780}{f}$
Total Element Length	$\frac{6022}{f}$	$\frac{15310}{f}$

DESIGN DATA. See diagram for dimension letter

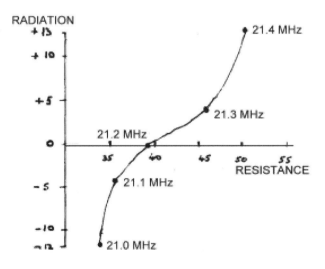

RADIATION RESISTANCE GRAPH

PETER DODD
G3LDO
SPRAT 30
SPRING 1982

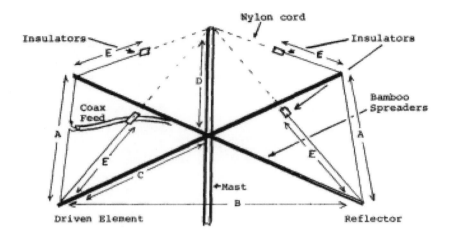

Nylon cord

Insulators

Insulators

E

E

D

Coax
Feed

Bamboo
Spreaders

A

A

E

E

C

Mast

B

Driven Element

Reflector

PERSPECTIVE VIEW

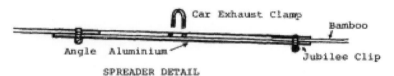

Car Exhaust Clamp

Bamboo

Angle Aluminium

Jubilee Clip

SPREADER DETAIL

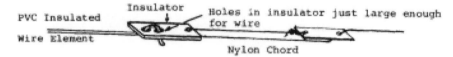

PVC Insulated

Insulator

Holes in insulator just large enough
for wire

Wire Element

Nylon Chord

INSULATOR DETAIL

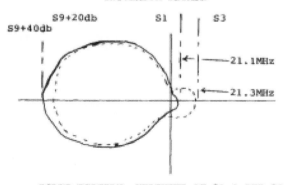

S9+20db

S1

S3

S9+40db

21.1MHz

21.3MHz

POLAR DIAGRAM, MEASURED AT 21.1 AND 21.3 MHz

This version is based on an idea by JG7UEA reported in CQ Magazine for June 1978. The original version was for 14 and 21 Mhz and it is claimed that it was 2 S-points up on a GP on 21 MHz. I modified the design and this gave problems on 21 MHz, but on 14 MHz the swr was acceptable. The JG7UEA version was made from four, 40 inch lengths of 3/8 inch aluminium tubing. The ends of these lengths are flattened and drilled so that they can be bolted together, except at the bottom of the loop where they are bolted to a small piece of insulating material. The connections to the tuned ciruit are made via these bolts, the tuned circuit itself being located in a small plastic box. A length of bamboo is used as a cross piece and the whole assembly is mounted on a short wooden pole. Capacitor C1 is 150p ,L1 and L3 are 3 turns and L2 is two turns, all 1½ inch diameter. The capacitor is used to resonate the loop to the desired band. My version was different. It was erected indoors in a ferro-concrete apartment building in Prague during last winter. The loop was made from 1mm stranded wire with PVC insulation. A 50p capacitor was used for C1. L1 and L2 were as per the original design, but L3 had to be made 5 turns to give a better swr on the co-ax feeder. The loop was hung up near the window , some degree of rotation being possible. Using 4w input on 14 MHz many F and G stations were worked, a clear path existing in these directions. Firing through the length of the building UA stations were worked, and also YO stations through the breadth of the building. Compared to my vertical on the roof of the building signals were 2 S-points down, but the loop was much lower and indoors. Maximum radiation was at rightangles to the plane of the loop. Tests lasted for a week.

G8PG comments. "The radiation resistance of this loop is very low, so conductor losses become very important. Using pieces of tubing bolted together is not suitable for a permanent outdoor installation because of corrosion losses in the joints. This problem can be overcome by making the loop from a continous length of good quality transmitting type co-axial cable with the inner and outer conductors soldered together; o.4 inch diameter co-ax is suitable. The connections to L1 and L2 must be carefully soldered, and the connection to the moving plates of C1 must be low loss, as all these items are in series with the loop resistance. Making L3 movable in relation to L1/L2 might help in reducing swr, and it might be worth trying a balun between L3 and the co-ax to the TX. A version with 10ft sides would allow interesting experiments on 7 MHz".

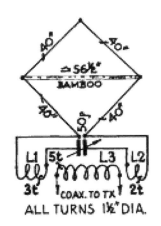

ALL TURNS 1½" DIA.

PETR DOUDERA
OK1DKW

SPRAT 21
WINTER 1979/80

MULTIBAND LOFT ANTENNA FOR 40/20/15/10m

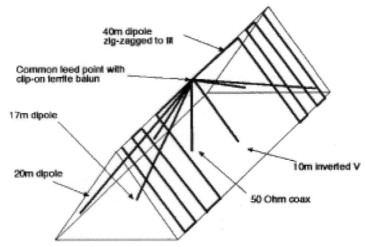

40m dipole zig-zagged to fit

Common feed point with clip-on ferrite balun

17m dipole

20m dipole

10m inverted V

50 Ohm coax

There is nothing new about this design, but it does bring together a few useful ideas. What surprises me is it works incredibly well - so well that I have yet to find another antenna that can beat it, including Capco Magnetic Loops, end feds and verticals for 10m all mounted outside. It will even load on 6m without an ATU.

It consists of separate half-wave dipoles for 40m, 20m, 17m and 10m, cut to 468(feet)/frequency x 95 percent. These are fed via RG58 50Ohm coax at a common feed point (this was built with a chocolate lock connector and a 35mm film canister as it was originally to be put up outside)

There are two large clip-on choke baluns at the feed point. The first trick is to zig-zag the 40m dipole up and down the loft space, once the first ten feet or so have been pulled out horizontally - this is where the greatest current is. The second is to make sure the end of each dipole is kept well away from the others. This helps bring down the SWR and improves the 10m performance dramatically. When it was originally put up they were all bundled together and although the 10m SWR was ok it was decidedly deaf. The third trick is to arrange the 10m dipole as an inverted-V – this has always worked well for me at three different QTHs. I used a staple gun to fasten the PVC coated wire to the rafters leaving the final six inches to dangle freely. SWR is less than 1.5:1 on all bands except 15m where the 40m dipole acts as three half waves and the SWR rises to about 2:1. It isn't a beam but it doesn't suffer from computer interference, either and it is a lively antenna, ideal for QRP and M3s. It lives in the main loft and a Capco 1.7m loop for 80m lives in the other garage roof space.

STEVE NICHOLS
G0KYA
SPRAT 111
SUMMER 2002

THE SKELTON CONE REVISITED

The basic idea of the Skeleton Cone comes from the R.S.G.B. Handbook (3rd edition), and has claims varying between 2.1dBs to 7dBs gain over a dipole on all bands. It has a 1:1 SWR over all bands, if used with an antenna tuner, and seems to have a pattern of 360 degrees.

I have been using a Skeleton Cone for sometime on the 40 and 80 metre bands. It is suspended from my tower at a height of 38 feet and is fed with 300 ohm twin lead to the homebrew Ultimate Transmatch. The ends of the antenna are 14 feet above earth, instead of the designed 18 feet, because of physical limitations at my QTH. I have worked JA, UA and KH6 with it and feel it should do well in the U.K.

Although the claimed gain figures are rather high, my Skeleton Cone has out performed a 130 feet inverted vee at 38-45 feet above ground, so I am sticking with it. For 160 metres the feeders could be tied together and the antenna operated top loaded or umbrella fashion. George, G3RJV describes the Skeleton Cone as two G5RVs, and it was his standard antenna for two years at his Birminhgham QTH.

The orignal version of the antenna was a modified G5RV. With double wires spread 33 degrees, greater bandwidth is achieved, and there is some filling in of the sharp nulls on the higher frequency bands. It is a good antenna with gain at the higher bands because it is electrically large. On 80 metres it is shorter than a half wavelength; 40 metres it is two half waves in phase; 20 metres it is three half wavelengths with six lobes and six nulls; 15 metres it is five half wavelengths long with ten lobes and nulls and on 10 metres it is two one and a half wavelengths long wires fed in phase.

The gain over a dipole in fact exists in certain directions where the lobes, are depending on the band in use. Another feature is that these lobes are at quite low angles, from 30 to 50 degrees, thereby enhancing a lot of propogation for DX.

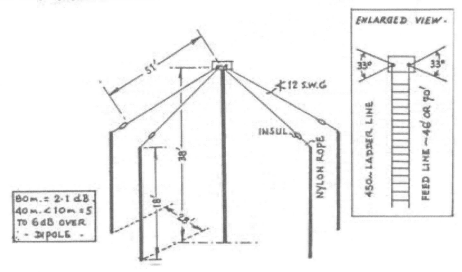

BOB SPIDELL
W6SKQ
SPRAT 43
SUMMER 1985

The Skeleton Cone can also be used with a balanced coax feed, (see diagram). I plan to use RG58U or RG59U coax because it would be lighter in weight. K6MDJ physically was able to ground the top of his feed system but I cannot, but I don't see any problem. I think this is a novel way to use a balanced feed system for fellows who think they have to use open wire line.

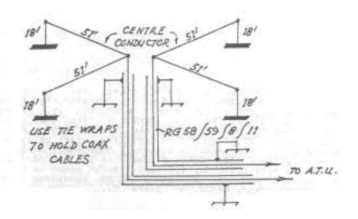

THE G3ESP
3.5-28MHz
SINGLE FEEDER
ANTENNA SYSTEM

Having got hold of a Kenwwod RS50 with an automatic ATU I set about developing a single co-axial feeder antenna system for all HF bands. This is shown in Fig 1. Wire a is approximately 40m long, providing a half wave at 80m, approximately three half waves at 30m. five half waves on 16m and seven half waves on 12m. With a little pruning this proved to be the case and the automatic ATU worked nicely. A half wave on 40m is approximately three half waves on 15m, so a suitable wire, wire b, was connected in parallel with the first wire. For 20 metres a third half wave was connected in parallel with the first two (wire c). There was then an unexpected bonus. With wires a,b, and c in position and trimmed, it was found that the combination loaded up nicely on 10m with no need to add a fourth wire. My plot of land is small, so the longer wires had to be drooped from the masts as shown.

W FARRAR
G3ESP
SPRAT 101
WINTER 1999/2000

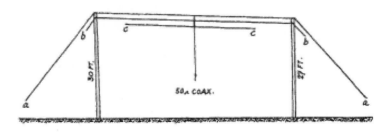

Fig. 1.

In the thirteenth edition of The ARRL Handbook, a 40 metre "sloper" system antenna is described by K1THQ. Although primarily intended for use on 40 and 80 metres, the system would make an ideal set up for the three HF bands for amateurs unable to erect beams or quads, especially for QRP use. Requiring only one centre support it is a directive antenna with up to 20dbs front to back ratio and several dbs of forward gain. Its advantages over the dipole inverted vee, loops etc., are quite considerable, although it is obviously not as good as beams and quads. The complete four sloper system is illustrated in fig. 1, and the measurements for the HF bands are shown in the table below. The sloping dipoles are cut exactly to half wavelength and fed with 52 ohm coaxial cable. The length of each feeder is critical as the three slopers not in use act as reflectors. The feed lines go to a relay box, which should be fixed to the centre support. The wiring for the relay box is shown in fig. 2 and for the control box at the operating position in fig. 3.

The Complete System

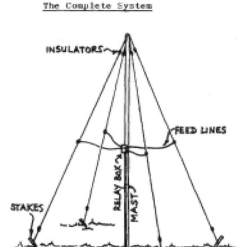

Fig. 1

Table of Measurements (feet)

Band	Antenna length	Feeder Length	Ideal Mast Height	Minimum Mast Height
80	131.4	72	100	40
40	66.6	36	60	30
20	33.3	18	40	25
15	22.2	13.5	35	20
10	16.8	9	30	15

Relay Box Diagram

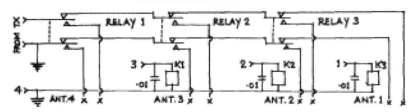

Fig. 2

CHRIS PAGE
G4BUE
SPRAT 25
WINTER 1980/1

The four sloping dipoles should be arranged for NW, NE, SW and SE as far as possible. It will be found that the SWR of each sloper is in the region of 2/3 to 1, but no attempt should be made to obtain a better SWR by altering the lengths of the antennas or the front to back ration will reduce.

Although I have no experience of a sloper system being used for the HF bands, I see no reason why they should not work as good as they have done on the LF bands. Although the centre support should be as high as possible, even with a 25 feet support the feed points for a 20 metre system will be quite high. Alternatively, a small mast on top of the chimney of the house

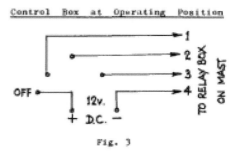

Control Box at Operating Position

Fig. 3

could be used, and the slopers dropped down each side of the house. By using thin wire they should be quite inconspicuous. When systems for 3.5MHz and 7MHz have been hung from the same mast no interaction between the two has been experienced, and it should, therefore, be possible to hang two (or more) HF systems off the same support, and use one control box but two (or more) relay boxes. If space does not permit four slopers for one system to be erected, then three or even two can be erected, these appearing to be much better than a single sloping dipole.

Fig. 4 illustrates the top view of the system, but of course the directions maybe altered to coincide with favoured directions of the operator or to fit into a garden, etc.

Once the system has been erected, the front to back ratio can be obtained by using each antenna in turn whilst a QSO is in progress, and comparing the different signal reports received. Alternatively some idea can be obtained by watching an S meter whilst each antenna

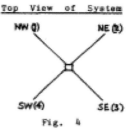

Top View of System

NW (1)   NE (2)

SW (4)   SE (3)

Fig. 4

is selected to receive a DX station. Another advantage of the system is that QRM is attenuated when attempting to work DXstations or weak QRP stations.

The original sloper system at G4BUE was at a previous QTH for QRO use. Then sufficient garden was available for a 7MHz system to be hung from a 60 feet crank up tower. The system worked very well indeed, even when the tower was lowered to 25 feet in bad weather. At this height the feed point of the slopers was only a few feet above ground, and the lower half of the antenna almost lying on the ground. See Method 'A' in Fig. 5.

Having discovered that the system works well on 7MHz with the tower at only 25 feet, I then tried a system for 3.5MHz from the 60 feet tower. The feed point to the 3.5MHz slopers was only a few feet above ground and the set up was in method 'B' of Fig. 5. This again was very successful enabling me to work DX that previous 3.5MHz antennas had not been able to do.

These results encouraged me to experiment further with slopers at my present QTH, but this time for QRP use. The HF beam at G4BUE is supported by the tower at a height of 35 feet (a condition of my planning permission prevents me from using the tower higher during daylight hours!). An inverted vee for 7MHz is hung from my TV mast on the house at a height of 30 feet, and whilst this is satisfactory for high angle local work, it proved very difficult to work DX with it.

Two slopers were constructed and hung from the tower just below the beam. One slopes to the NW to the USA and the other to the NE and Asiatic Russia. Due to the small size of my present garden it was not possible to string out the slopers as I had done previously, but I folded them back on themselves towards the tower, as in method 'B' of Fig. 5. The results have been quite staggering. During the 1979 CQ WW CW Contest I worked 39 stations in the USA on 7MHz with five watts input from the Argonaut, and during the 1980 ARRL CW Contest I worked 69 USA stations in 16 States, VE, UA9 and UL7.

One bonus of the system has been when working QRP stations in The U.K. or Western Europe using vertical antennas. The sloper system gives an increase of up to three S points on both transmit and receive over the inverted vee. Some of the biggest LF signals out of the USA use switchable sloping dipoles, including systems for 1.8MHz!! I would be very interested to hear from members who have used this system, or try it on the HF bands.

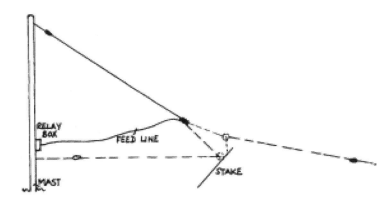

PARKING LOT PORTABLE VERTICAL

Many folks have asked me about the PLPV so here goes:

Like many of you I try to find the time to do as much QRPing as possible given the schedules of work and family. Although I have been a ham on and off since 1957 I never have been active during a sunspot cycle. I was bound and determined to be active this cycle and find a way to maximize my operating time. The only way possible for me to increase my operating time was at lunchtime near work. Since like many of you I work in an urban environment I am faced with lots of concrete. My one restriction was not to have a BIG antenna on the car permanently. Bob Edwards W4ED showed the North Georgia (NOGA) QRP group a portable set-up for his SLA vertical that showed promise but it did require a car and the antenna had to be adjacent to the car. He used a frame/stand that was held steady by a car tire resting on the antenna support frame. I was looking for something a little more flexible. Something that could be operated from a car, in the event of rain or bad weather but, also could be operated from anywhere it could be hauled. I like to bike ride and trail hike so I was looking for a method of setting up an antenna that was independent of trees and other local supports.

The design criteria:

1. Collapsible to less than 4 ft
2. Multi-band capability (at least 40,30,20,15,10 mtrs)
3. No tuner required
4. Coax fed (RG-58)
5. Light enough to be backpacked or carried on bicycle
6. Set-up or breakdown time less than 5 minutes
7. Self-supporting (requiring no external supports)
8. Low profile for storage - "small golf bag" size
9. Low Price - Less than $40

Using the idea of the SLA-type collapsible fishing pole as a vertical support I wondered how could I achieve the other criteria: self-supporting, quick setup/band change times and no tuner.

I came on the idea of a foldable wooden support structure that would hold the fishing pole erect and stable in reasonable winds. The fishing pole selected from a local Bass fishing store was a multi-section Carpie Pole made of black plastic that collapsed down to less than 4 ft and extended is almost 20 ft. I think any of the pole brands that have been mentioned on the various SLA articles would work.

I initially built a wooden foldable base that worked but was too heavy. At Home Depot I found some 1X1X36-inch aluminium angle that looked promising. Using four pieces I formed the base. Using a fifth piece I cut it in pieces and made a square base frame 3X3 inch and hinged the four 3ft pieces to the small square base. The remaining 2-ft piece I bolted to the small base (not hinged). I made a wooden Tee to screw the four base legs together so the base and legs were

SAM BILLINGSLEY
AE4GX
SPRAT 99
SUMMER 1999

fairly rigid and self-supporting. The 2ft section was vertical and the resulting structure looked like a four radial GP sitting on the ground. The fishing pole was cable tied to the 2-ft angle so the vertical when extended reached about 20ft. With the wooden Tee unscrewed from the four legs the legs fold towards the fishing pole. When then pole is collapsed and the legs are folded the entire structure is about 4ft tall and about 6-8 inches in diameter. It can easily be picked up with one hand. It's very light.

I had read that verticals with a limited number of above ground radials being more effective than verticals with a similar number of radials on the ground so I decided to have the base of the vertical be about 1.5 to 2 ft off the ground and that any radials would be slightly sloping downward towards to ground at the outer ends. I decided on initially trying two radials on opposite sides of the base.

The antenna would be coax fed with 50-ohm RG-58 and coax sections would be available to cover varying distances from 20 ft to 70 ft from the base of the antenna to the transceiver. This arrangement would accommodate a variety of set-up conditions with the shortest amount of coax.

The no tuner requirement meant pretuning the antenna for the bands of interest. Initially I tried the multi-wire parallel configuration with individual wires cut to each band but the interaction seems to be too tough to solve. So I cut a 1/4 wavelength for the highest band of interest (10 mtrs). One wire for the vertical section and two for the radials and attached them to the coax at the base in the classic inverted Y configuration. The vertical wire connected to the inter-conductor of the coax and one end of the radial wires to the outer shield of the coax. To decouple the coax feedline from the antenna I made a RF choke by wrapping about six turns 6 inches in diameter of coax and tapping them together. With my trusty MFJ SWR analyzer I checked the arrangement for freq vs min SWR. On all bands tried I could get a low SWR but using the book formula length where a quarter wave (ft) equals 468/freq(in MHz)/2. The problem I noticed was that the frequency at the low SWR point was always lower than expected by the formula. But by careful pruning of the radials and the vertical section I could get the antenna to have a low SWR < 1.5 to 1 in the frequency range of interest. I then calculated and added sections to all three elements to get to the next lower band and prune for SWR in the new frequency band of interest. I have done this for three bands to date (20,15,10). So you have one, second or three little wire segments depending on the band. How do you keep them together, yet apart, for the unneeded segments? My wife's sewing box had some lightweight elastic band tape (looks like stretchy string) that is used for making or mending expandable clothing. I took a four inch section and attached the end or the wire segments by simply knotting the wire and the elastic leaving about one inch of wire over the end of the knotted area. To the wire ends I crimped on some small quick disconnects (from RS). When completed the connected wire segments can be pulled taut and the segments will be apart a few inches. To give the horizontal radials a little extra support I taped the segments to a piece of lightweight nylon rope. The vertical is clipped at the very top of the extended pole to a section of elastic connected to the last wire segment. When fully extended the segments are stretched a small amount. To change from band to band you simply collapse the pole and connect the needed segments and re-extend the pole. The radials are similarly connected. Since the all the segments are already inplace the operation takes less than a minute. The pole can handle a 1/4 wave length vertical wire down through the 20 mtr band (i.e. 16.6ft). To accomplish the remaining bands (40 and 30 mtrs) you need to form a loading coil and an additional wire segment above the coil. These can be made in a quick disconnect manner previously described. The 40 and 30 mtr segments should be made separately to simplify the antenna. If these lower bands are rarely used I would keep them aside and not complicate the vertical or radial segments. But if operation is desired routinely you can have them in place just like the wire segments for the higher bands.

The results of the antenna have been better than expected. QRPTTF and ARS Bumblebee events have proven its effectiveness. More importantly I can go out at lunch and catch some QRP action.

THE BOBTAIL

THE BOBTAIL IS USUALLY REGARDED AS A SINGLE BAND DIRECTIONAL ANTENNA, but Mike G0ROT, has been using his 7 MHz version on 3.5 MHz by grounding the far end as shown in the diagram below. This gives a sort of half-loop configuration, with radiation angles giving excellent results around Europe. One could also use this idea to operate the antenna on all hf bands above its design frequency either as a half loop (far end grounded) or as an inverted U random wire (far end not grounded). Mike uses a Z-match atu with his.

MIKE DAVIS
G0ROT
SPRAT 81
WINTER 1994/5

During the last year I have been engaged in finding out my best way how to receive Grimeton Radio, SAQ, the historic VLF CW radio station located on the southwest coast of Sweden, still employing a so-called alternator engine to generate a frequency of 17,2 kHz [1]. Whilst a loop aerial gave good results, an active aerial on a wooden pole, about 10 meters from the house and 4 meters high, proved to be even less prone to certain forms of interference from the mains.

My first active antenna has been the Mini Whip [2] proposed by Roelof Bakker, PA0RDT. But soon I became inspired by an article in [3] by Marco Bruno, IK1ODO, to try an operational amplifier in the active part of such an antenna. Active aerials have to pass many r.f. signals simultaneously, and intermodulation would result if the aerial were driven up to its limits. The greatest advantage of employing an operational amplifier I saw in the typical feedback of those amplifiers from output to input which is rather difficult to achieve in active aerials using few discrete active components. This feedback would allow to pre-distort the input signal to deliver an output almost identical to the original wave form.

Table 1

Operational Amplifier	OP27	LT1252
C1	2,6 pF	16 pF
C2	9 pF	4 pF
R1	150 kΩ	0...47Ω
R2	1 MΩ	12 kΩ

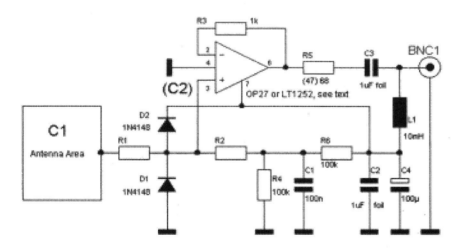

Active Aerial using Operational Amplifier

HA-JO BRANDT
DJ1ZB

SPRAT 130
SPRING 2007

According to table 1 the circuit in fig 1 can be used in two different ways. When using the OP27, R1 and C2, the input capacitance of the OP27, will form an RC low-pass filter with a cutoff frequency of about 500 kHz. Supply current is just 4 mA. As the cutoff frequency of the OP27 is 8 MHz the cutoff frequency may be increased by reducing R1. The antenna area C1 can be as small as 900 square millimeters. Following the example given by PA0RDT the circuitry and the aerial can be built or etched on the same pcb.

The LT1252 is an operational amplifier with a cutoff frequency of 100 MHz. Wayne Burdick, N6KR, has used it already in 1997 for his SST QRP transceiver. This IC can be employed to realize an active aerial operating from 10 kHz up to 30 MHz. R1 will be zero in this case, or have a low value just to serve as a protection resistor for the clamp diodes D1 and D2 in case of a dangerous high voltage inrush. The value of the feedback resistor R3 in fig 1, in spite of being equal for both operational amplifiers in this example, depends on different considerations, according to sources [4; 5; 6]. As the output resistance of an operational amplifier becomes very low due to the feedback applied, resistor R5 provides a match to the cable impedance and also decouples the feedback path from the capacity of the cable, important for the stability of the amplifier [5]. Current drain of the LT1252 will be 10 mA.

Some readers may wonder about the low value of R2 in this second solution. The problem with this large bandwidth aerial is that the atmospheric noise at 10 kHz is up to 50 dB higher than at 30 MHz. If the active antenna area is reduced to avoid overload of the aerial at low frequencies, sensitivity at HF will be lowered correspondingly. The reduction of R2, however, is a means to reduce sensitivity at lower frequencies but to keep the antenna area large for better sensitivity at HF. Keep in mind that the capacitive divider C1/C2 will also lower its reactance towards higher frequencies. With this solution the antenna area may be made as large as 6000 square millimeters without overloading the aerial.

The performance of the antenna area concerning intermodulation can be controlled without the need of a spectrum analyzer. When intermodulation is caused by strong HF broadcast transmitters in late afternoon, carriers may appear at VLF almost every 10 kHz. If medium wave broadcast transmitters are the cause of intermodulation in the evening, other carriers may show up at VLF almost every 9 kHz. Furthermore, anybody may calculate the mixing products of strong local radio signals (f1 +/- f2; 2f1 - f2; 2f2 - f1) and try to detect them in a general coverage receiver. The aim should be to reduce these carriers or mixing products by reducing the antenna area (and/or R2) until they are barely discernible and will not harm normal reception on these frequencies. After doing this, sensitivity at VLF should be controlled and R2 altered if necessary. For optimum sensitivity at VLF it should be possible in a noise-free environment and installation to receive the signals of the russian "Omega" navigation system (short CW dashes) at 11,90, 12,65, and 14,88 kHz. Receiving these signals is almost a prerequisite for good reception of SAQ. It should be noted that the output of an active aerial will increase by about 6 dB when its height above ground is doubled. This may also influence the optimum permissible antenna area.

How we can relate the antenna area of the pcb to a capacity in pF? According to PA0RDT an area of 1200 square millimeters corresponds to a rod or whip aerial of 30 cm length and 2 mm thickness and will have a capacity of 3,2 pF.

The capacitiy of a whip aerial CA may be calculated using the formula

$$CA \sim \frac{55pF*h}{\ln(1,15*h/D)}$$

In this formula h is the length and D the thickness of the whip, all dimensions in meter. This formula has also been used to calculate C1 in table 1. C2 has been taken from the datasheets plus 1 pF for protection diodes D1 and D2.

Construction of the active aerial follows the example of PA0RDT. The PCB containing aerial and circuit is housed within a plastic drain pipe, with a BNC connector (and a BNC grounding lug for the screen contact) mounted in the lower end cup. My experimental models are using a pipe diameter of 50 mm because locally available. The picture may illustrate this. The small tube in the upper left, with a length of 105 mm, is sufficient for the OP27 aerial. The PCB measures 85 mm x 45 mm, about 20 mm length are needed for the antenna area. The LT1252 aerial will need the short tube and an additional longer tube of 215 mm length. For ease of changing antenna areas this PCB has been divided into two parts, 70 mm x 45 mm for the circuit and 135 mm x 45 mm for the aerial; both to be screwed together with an overlap of 10 mm. The PCB with the circuit is soldered to the BNC connector at the lower end, either directly or via short semi-stiff wires. Therefore two solder pads have been provided at the lower end, one in the centre and one on one side, corresponding to the contacts of the BNC connector and its grounding lug. I have preferred to round the upper end of the active aerial, to avoid any peaks or discontinuities in the surrounding electric field.

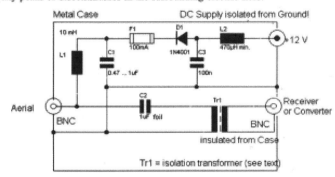

Power Feed in Metal Case for Active Aerial

Fig 2 shows the circuit to feed the active aerial via the coaxial cable. L2 prevents HF picked up by the 12 V line to be coupled to the receiver. Because of this danger a metal case should be used for the power feed unit. D1 is a protection against wrong polarity. For low-noise reception below 80 kHz the isolation transformer Tr1 may be necessary for low noise reception, when the cable braid is grounded not only outside the house, as demanded by PA0RDT, but also via a safety ground of the receiver in the shack. In this case an isolated BNC connector has to be used at the receiver output of the case. For VLF reception both windings of Tr1 should have an inductivity of about 1,5 mH. If the input impedance of the receiver or converter should deviate from the cable impedance Tr1 should be altered as necessary.

When comparing active with passive aerials at HF one will find that some stations deliver a signal differing by just an S-unit or two whilst other stations perform extremely different. This is due to the angle and the polarisation of the incident wave. Therefore many manufacturers combine active whip aerials with dipoles. In this respect the simple active whip aerial seems to be reliable below 1,6 MHz only, where vertical polarisation is employed in most cases.

[1]   http://www.alexander.n.se
[2]   Infos about the Mini Whip: roelof@ndb.demon.nl
[3]   http://www.vlf.it/op027a.htm
[4]   www.analog.com Datasheet OP27
[5]   LTC Design Note DN46 "Current Feedback Amplifiers Do's and Don'ts" by William Gross www.linear.com
[6]   www.linear.com Datasheets of LT1252 and similar operational amplifiers

The antenna section consists of a 20 foot alloy mast with top loading and base tuning (Fig 1). The base is made from a sloping shoulder wine bottle such as a champagne bottle. The mast is guyed with 4 guys each made from multi-strand polyethylene cord, which is weather resistant and an excellent insulator,attached to the pole by a suitable clamp. The top loading unit is based on a 1 foot length of timber of suitable diameter to fit into the top of the mast. It has holes drilled in it to take three, 5 foot long garden canes which support the top loading windings (Fig 2). These canes are wedged and glued into position. The unit uses 6 turns of 2 foot radius to provide capacity loading, and 3 turns of 1 foot radius to provide inductive loading (Fig 2).

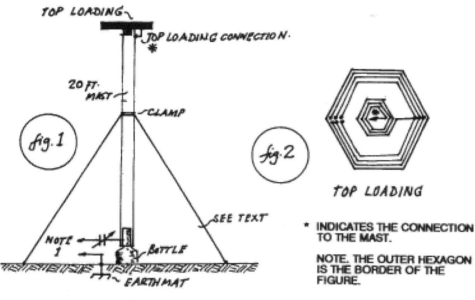

fig.1

fig.2

TOP LOADING

* INDICATES THE CONNECTION TO THE MAST.

NOTE. THE OUTER HEXAGON IS THE BORDER OF THE FIGURE.

COMPLETE ANTENNA

NOTE 1 - TO G.D.O LOOP, FEEDER OR A.T.U.

Theloading coils are wound with 18 swg enamelled copper wire, connetions to the mast being via the screw which secures the 1 foot long wooden centre piece to the mast. This connection must be thoroughly weatherproofed. The antenna is tuned to resonance by means of a variable capacitor of at least 200p, mounted in a weatherproof plastic box attached to the base of the mast. One side of this capacitor is connected to the mast and the other to the live side of a coaxial connector mounted on the box, the other side of this connector going to the earthing system. Once again goodweatherproofing is vital. This co-axial connector provides termination for the cable back to the rig. The antenna is resonated by disconnecting the cable to the rig and replacing it with a single turn loop of wire. A g.d.o can then be coupled to this loop and the variable capacitor adjusted until resonance is obtained in the 7 MHz band. If resonance is not obtained add a single turn to the inductive loading. The more efficient the earth system the better will be the results with this antenna. I use a lot of chicken wire which has been allowed to sink into the ground, but radials, either elevated and/or buried or a combination of radials and earth spikes can also be used. Feeding methods for good swr can use either an electrical half wave of co-ax or an a.t.u can be mounted in the box at the base of the mast.

D VANCE
GI3XZM
SPRAT 119
SUMMER 2004

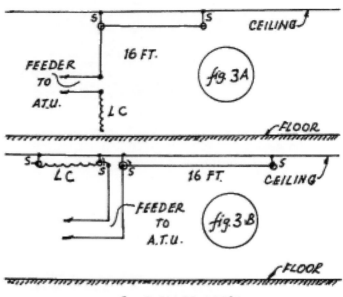

FEEDER
TO
A.T.U.

CEILING

16 FT.

fig 3A

LC

FLOOR

S
LC
S
S

16 FT.

CEILING
S

FEEDER
TO
A.T.U.

fig 3B

FLOOR

S : SUPPORT CORDS

Either gives good results.
The loading system raises the feed point impedance (in
this model calculated at around 28 ohms) , which improves radiation efficiency
although this also depends on how good the earthing system is. This loading
can also be adopted to load a range of shortened antennas, both horizontal
and vertical . If you try it please let us know your results. (Acknowledgements
to Radcom for some design ideas.)

Many radio amateurs begin their interest in radio through short wave listening and many short wave listeners remain SWLs. Although I am a ham my main interest, for 25 years has been short wave listening. In our towns it is often difficult to install a good antenna system so active antennas are used.

Most of them are only amplifiers, broadband and high gain BUT still only amplifiers. In these cases when the antenna is turned on the signals increases but the noise increases too. In particular during the night when MW transmitters are arriving from nearby countries, with many KW, and in the day if the SWL is unfortunately located in MW transmitter area. How do we solve this problem and achieve high gain for weak signals without being overloaded by a local station? By using an active BROAD BAND ANTENNA that doesn't amplify the MW region. I have used many types of active antennas but last year I got the December issue of "Electronic Design" which described this circuit.

This is my version of the circuit - which works very well.

The theory says that a short dipole's polar pattern isn't a "8" figure as in the quarter wave dipole, BUT has much sharp nulls that allow you to null-out the undesired signal by rotating the dipole .

At other hand the short dipole (less than 1 meter) has a too high impedance to drive the 50 ohm receiver's input direct.

Therefore, dual FETs are used to translate the high impedance to the low rx impedance but with the FETs, we receive a low signal level .

This level is amplified by a dual input wide band video amplifier (LM733) and the dual output of the IC must be transformed from dual to single ended.

As presented, the circuit gain can be selected:

For strong signal some amplification amount (9 db) is selected by SPDT switch in the LG position.

When high gain is needed (20db) the SPDT must be switched on HG position.

When we need high gain in the short wave range BUT need eliminates MW-interference the FS position must be used. In fact in this case the amplification is 9 db up to 1,6 MHz and 20 db at upper frequencies.

VERY NICE! - you can get high gain SW amplification and low MW amplification.

The frequency response is very flat from 200 kHz to 35 MHz (+- 0,2 db) and +- 0,4 db down up to 60 MHz. The gain is flat up to 25 MHz and –3db at 50 MHz. The maximum signal level is 500mV(!) rms in to 75 Ω load.

My version of the antenna is for external installation, I used a pair of dipoles switched by relays and is N-S E-W oriented (ideal for Italy) but maybe a small TV rotator is better.

The power is supplied a separate multipole cable (in this case) but for single dipole version the power can be supplied by coax cable as shown.

 Alignment: the 47 k trimmer must be rotate for equal clipping of the signal just past the maximum level.

MARCO ELEUTERI
IK0VSV
SPRAT 101
WINTER 1999/2000

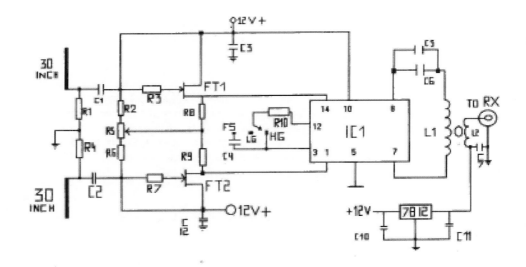

POWER SUPPLY SYSTEMS VIA COAX

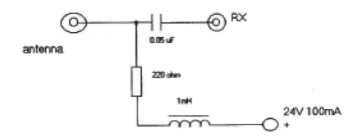

components list

R1-4	5 M
R2-6	330K
R5	47K
R3-7	330K
R8-9	4.3K
R10	330

FT1-2   fet n channel 2N5246 or any similar whit Idss<2mA
        (BF245)

IC1   LM733 or LM733C (C versione is for civil use 0° to +70°range)

C1-2	100P	C6	0.05 uF	C12	0.1 uF
C3	0.1 uF	C7	0.05 uF		
C4	33P	C10	1.5 uF	L1	36 truns of n°24 enameled wire
C5	0.47uF	C11	0.47uF	L2	9 turns same wire
					on T50/2 or better toroidal core

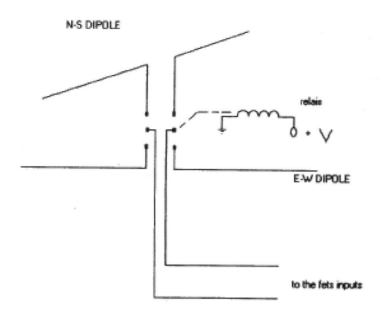

N-S DIPOLE

relais

E-W DIPOLE

to the fets inputs

Practical details of the Active Antenna

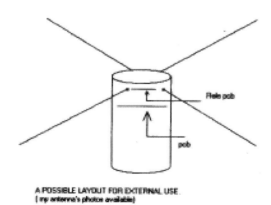

Field pob

pob

A POSSIBLE LAYOUT FOR EXTERNAL USE.
(my antenna's photos available)

'SARDINE RECEIVER' ANTENNA

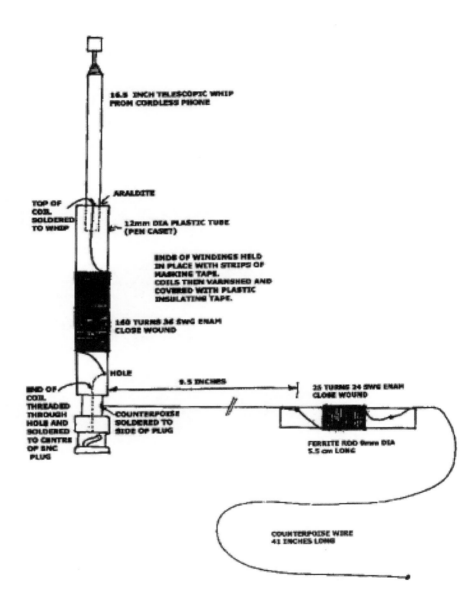

16.5 INCH TELESCOPIC WHIP FROM CORDLESS PHONE

ARALDITE

TOP OF COIL SOLDERED TO WHIP

12mm DIA PLASTIC TUBE (PEN CASE?)

ENDS OF WINDINGS HELD IN PLACE WITH STRIPS OF MASKING TAPE. COILS THEN VARNISHED AND COVERED WITH PLASTIC INSULATING TAPE.

160 TURNS 36 SWG ENAM CLOSE WOUND

HOLE

9.5 INCHES

35 TURNS 34 SWG ENAM CLOSE WOUND

END OF COIL THREADED THROUGH HOLE AND SOLDERED TO CENTRE OF BNC PLUG

COUNTERPOISE SOLDERED TO SIDE OF PLUG

FERRITE ROD 9mm DIA 5.5 cm LONG

COUNTERPOISE WIRE 41 INCHES LONG

DUNCAN WALTERS
G4DFV
SPRAT 116
AUTUMN 2003

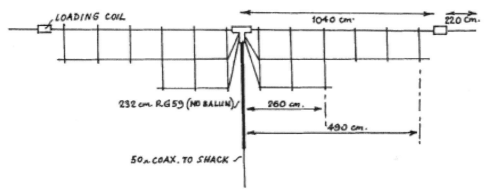

Figure 1

This antenna was developed to allow 5-band operation with no ATU.
Owing to space limitations the flat top is only 15m long, the
ends forming an inverted U. It is a nest of dipoles with the wires
spaced to give minimum interaction; wire lengths are not what you
might expect. The top wire uses loading coils and wires to allow
80m operation, the coils acting as isolating chokes on 40m. Experiment
with coil size to get the right inductance for your particular
site. The top wire also resonates near 15m and the quarter wave of
75 ohm co-ax transforms the impedance for this band. The remainin ++
wires cover 20m and 10m. The spacers are made from plastic A4 size
paper binding strips (Fig 2). Make the wires 10% longer initially,
then adjust to resonance by bending the wire back on itself. Adjust
the 10m wire first, then work down to the 80m wire as this provides
minimum interaction between wires. In my model I achieved an SWR
of 1.2-1 or better over the CW portion of all the bands covered.

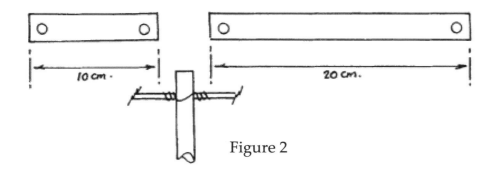

Figure 2

The WARC bands could also be covered by using my T-match ATU,
but the losses were obviously somewhat higher.

++ W2XM ,Hints & Kinks For The Radio Amateur p7-25.
+++ GoNEZ, SPRAT 68, p14.

**MA EALES
M0AJL
SPRAT 101
WINTER 1999/2000**

A USEFUL SHORT SLOPER FOR 7MHz

With a length of only 4.87 m and a counterpoise of the same length this antenna is ideal for restricted space and it has worked well, particularly as a sloper. It is shown in Fig. 1. The radiator is made from a length of slotted 300 ohm ribbon feeder, with the two conductors soldered together at the end. This joint should be weatherproofed. The tuner consists of coil L1 and capacitor C1. L1 is 20 turns of 16 swg wire spaced to occupy 80mm on a 2.5 cm diameter former.. The inner of the co-ax feeder from the rig is is soldered to the tenth turn .. Capacitor C1 is of 250 pf.. The components are mounted on a piece of printed circuit board of suitable size, and this in turn is mounted in a plastic food container with all the holes for input and exit wires sealed with glue. With the component values shown the antenna will also resonate on 3.5 MHz, but on air tests have not been made on this band.

(This one would also seem to have possibilities for /P work. G8PG)

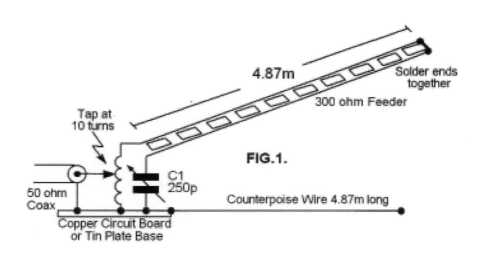

FIG.1.

A UPTON
G3UZU
SPRAT 126
SPRING 2006

This is a two turn, diamond quad-shaped loop, fed via a Faraday coupling coil made from coaxial cable. It is tuned with the aid of a 1,000pF vacuum capacitor which is operated from a gearbox turned by a small electric motor. The loop lightweight support frame is made from lengths of 20mm plastic electrical conduit tube pushed into a central 4-way electrical junction box. See right.

The two turns of the loop are made from PVC covered multi-strand copper wire. They are each approximately 20ft 6in (6.25m) in length, and are connected in parallel at the tuning capacitor. They are spaced from each other by three T pieces inserted into the ends of the conduit pipes, drilled with holes 1in (2.5cm) apart. If necessary additional spacers cut from C plastic and drilled with holes 1in (2.5cm) apart can be fitted. The loop is tuned with the aid of a 12V motor which operates a pair of reduction gears, one attached to its gearbox and the other attached to the vacuum capacitor. The capacitor, gearbox, motor and its power supply are mounted in a large plastic box. See pictures below. This box also contains a base mount for the vertical member of the loop frame, the weight being sufficient to hold the loop upright when it is used INDOORS. More substantial anchoring and much more careful waterproof would be required if it is to be mounted outdoors.

The motor and gear wheels were bought at a local model shop, but obtaining the vacuum capacitor involved some work at local radio rallies and reading of radio magazines until one was found. These two pictures show the arrangements inside the plastic box.

DEREK LOVE
G0DRA
SPRAT 127
SUMMER 2006

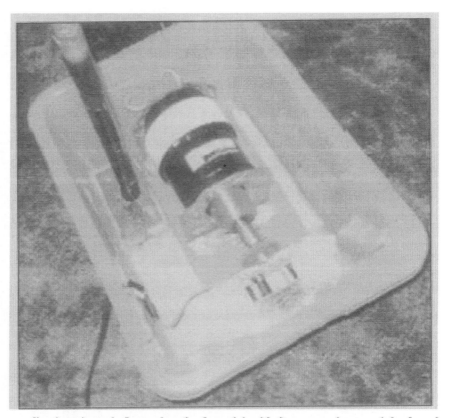

The coupling loop is made from a length of coaxial cable long enough to reach back to the rig, the last 4 ft (1.22m) of which are formed into a coupling loop by soldering the inner conductor to the outer screen (see the first picture). As it has not been possible to fully waterproof the system so far, it is mounted in my loft and orientated so that it fires roughly east and west. The gearing gives a very slow tuning rate. The original tuning was carried out with an MFJ antenna analyser with the rig SWR meter being used once the setting for the two bands was found. On 7MHz a bandwidth of 30kHz for an SWR not exceeding 1.5:1 was obtained, the equivalent bandwidth on 3.5MHz being 20kHz. As stated above, the loop is not rotated, but positioned so as to fire into Europe. On 7MHz it gives good EU results and is also good into Ireland off the back. On 3.5MHz it gives good results to the UK.

A Second G0DRA loop – outdoors and HF

This one is an outdoor delta loop covering 14, 18 and 21MHz. The total length is 48 ft (14.63M) of wire, plus an open wire feeder to the shack, where it is fed via a Z-match. The top is secured to a fibre-glass spar, which is hoisted on to a fibre-glass mast. The whole assembly is very light and can be raised and lowered quickly if required, the two ends of the lower section being secured to guys. It works well. (Readers with a nautical interest will see here a radio version of the Junk rig beloved of single handed yachtsmen. The design also seems to offer other useful possibilities for /P operation – G8PG)

If your location has no room (or is too cluttered) for a full length low dipole and you still want to explore near-vertical incidence skywave (NVIS) propagation [1,2,3] on HF, then you might like to try aerial designs based on the inwardly inclined dual monopole (IIDM) concept [4,5]. This idea was progressed with the aid of Roy Lewallen's (W7EL) excellent aerial design tool EZNEC™ for the PC [6], which so easily allows an experimenter to conduct 'armchair' based explorations before committing designs to wire.

Papers in [4,5] give details of far field (FF) patterns – the near ideal being a sphere resting on the ground at the aerial's location – and discuss VSWR and multi-band capabilities [esp. in 5]. E.g., the same aerial used at 40m for NVIS can, without further adjustment (apart from ATU tuning), exploit horizontal sidelobes that appear at second harmonic and higher frequencies (14, 18 and 21MHz) for skip working. Paper 4 explored an earlier unbalanced feed design which performed well but lacked the NVIS FF lobe stability with frequency of later [5,7] balanced feed designs (e.g., Figs. 1, 2 and 3). Pre-match capacitors (Cm) in the matching unit M of Fig. 4 should be high voltage types and may be constructed from co-axial cable as part of the MQ and MP connections. The values provide a 50 ohm match in each case, using an ATU for fine tuning. Paper [5] also demonstrates the robustness of the IIDM design to changes in configuration, including element elevation and sideways tilt. Most locations, especially cluttered ones, have their own idiosyncrasies. At the home QTH, environmental constraints (beloved of XYLs) include flowerbeds and footpaths. Therefore to avoid strangling visitors (the friendly ones) the grounded leg of a folded element (c.f. Fig. 2) had to be extended and re-routed down a shed wall. But checking via EZNEC™ predicted little effect on the FF pattern. The modified aerial still works fine and remains the one for main HF use.

Figs. 1a,b, 2 and 3 show 7.05MHz IIDM aerials along with captions giving details of wire lengths. If it turns out that what is shown would not fit into your back garden, the design is sufficiently flexible to allow even further modifications – but check with your simulator program (e.g., EZNEC™ 3.0 or 4.0) first! Thus for further height reduction the unfolded DM aerial can be top-loaded with horizontal wires and folded versions can employ 'squared off' elements.

References:
[1]   Fiedler, DM and Hagn, GH (1996). Beyond line-of-sight propagation: modes and antennas. In: Fiedler, DM. And Farmer, E.J. (Eds.) Near Vertical Incidence Skywave Communication: Theory, Techniques and Validation. Worldradio, CA. pp10-17.
[2]   Austin, BA and Murray, KP (1998).   The application of characteristic-mode techniques to vehicle-mounted NVIS antennas. IEEE Antennas and Propagation Magazine, 40 (1) pp. 7-21.
[3]   Pat Hawker (2001). Cloud-Warming Antennas, Technical topics, RadCom, Sept.
[4]   Telfer, DJ and Austin, BA (2001). Novel antenna design for near vertical incidence skywave (NVIS) HF communications. Proc. 2nd International Conf. on Advanced System Design, Glasgow.
[5]   Telfer, DJ and Spencer, JWS (2004). Properties and performance of a new compact HF aerial design for multi-band operation. Proc. 4th Int. Conf. on Advanced System Design, University of Glasgow. [PDF obtainable from www.cims.org.uk]
[6]   Lewallen, R. 2004. Antenna analysis software suite from EZNEC.com (Internet).
[7]   Telfer,DJ. 'Multiple Monopole Aerial.' UK Patent GB2375235. April 2004.

DUNCAN TELFER
G0SIB/G8ATH
SPRAT 121
WINTER 2004/5

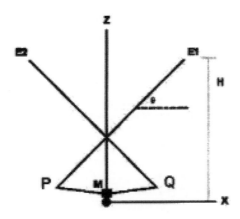

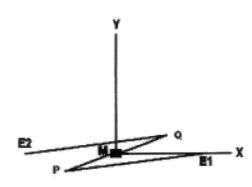

Fig.1a Unfolded DM aerial for 40m : θ=45°,
H=1040cm, E1(P)=E2(Q)=1293cm,
H(M)=60cm, H(P,Q)=100cm, PM=MQ=340cm,
separation at tops of E1,E2 = 1090cm.

Fig.1b Unfolded DM aerial, plan view.
Separation of E1 and E2 at crossover point
is 115cm. The horizontal displacements (Y)
of P and Q are -100cm and +100cm,
respectively, from X-axis.

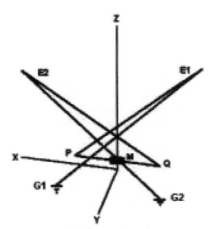

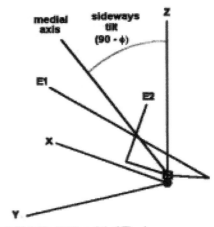

Fig.2 Folded DM aerial with grounded wires
E1(G1) = 1255cm, E2(G2) = 1228cm.
Driven wires   E1(P) = 1149cm,
E2(Q) = 1178cm. G1,G2 are 260cm
from the PQ (Y=0) axis.
X-separation between G1,G2 = 630cm.
PM = MQ = 260cm. Ht (Z) of E1,E2 = 900cm
and separation of skewed tops = 1072cm,
with top of E1 directly above the (Y=0) axis
and top of E2 above (Y=260cm) axis.
Heights (Z) of P, M and Q are each 56cm.

Fig.3 Unfolded DM aerial of Fig. 1a
with sideways medial axis tilt of 45°.
PMQ parameters in Fig. 1a are retained –
only the elements E1 and E2 are tilted,
and lengthened slightly to 1297cm
to improve impedance match.
Cm values in the matching unit
should be reduced slightly to 41pF
(see also Fig. 4).

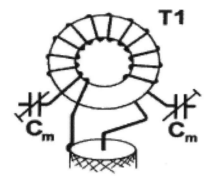

Fig. 4. Matching unit M may use a toroidal transformer or choke balun. Capacitors Cm =43pF for DM aerial of Fig. 1 and 63pF for Fig. 2.

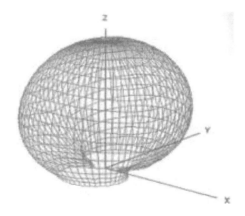

Fig.5 7.05MHz FF pattern for DM aerial of Fig.1, assuming perfect ground. The other two aerials have closely similar FF patterns [see Ref. 5].

A SINGLE FEED ANTENNA FOR 3.5 TO 21MHz

The antenna uses 20m traps and 100 uH loading coils to cover
the bands indicated, and gives good performance on all of them.
To give maximum results it is used with a suitable atu. It does
not work well on 28 Mhz, so a separate antenna is used on that
band (It might be worth connecting the two feeder wires together
and using it as a T antenna on 28 Mhz. Ed).The placing of the
100 uH loading coils was determined with the aid of the 13th
Edition of the ARRL Antenna Book, as was the winding details.
The traps are also described in this book. They are wound on
T68-2 ferrite rings and initially tuned to 14.3MHz. Encapsulation
brings this figure down to 14.2 MHz. Both the coils and the
traps are encapsulated in in lengths of 20mm plastic tubing with
the aid of potting resin. The feeder is made from twin figure of
eight loudspeaker cable (2 x 42/0.2 wire)which has an impedance
close to 70 ohms. Ordinry 70 ohm twin feeder could also be used
if desired. Even without the atu performance on 20 and 80 metres
was good, and even better with the atu. Performance on 40
metres was really good and the antenna works well on 15m,
although the atu is essential on this band. The details of the
antenna are shown in Figure 1 below.

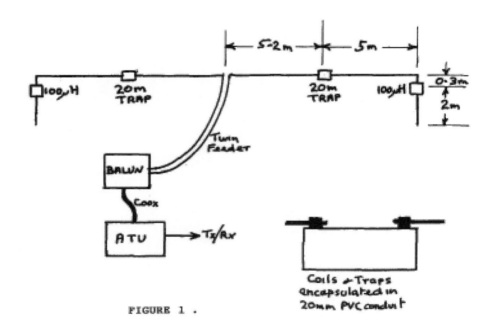

FIGURE 1 .

JIM BRETT
G0TFP
SPRAT 112
AUTUMN 2002

A NON-GROUNDED FOLDED NVIS AERIAL FOR 40m

As many of us know, the effort in deploying earth posts, grounding mats, etc., generally exceeds that in erecting the aerial itself! Although the folded inwardly inclined dual monopole (IIDM) aerial in SPRAT 121 [1] has been in use at my QTH for about 4 years, the grounding points are attached to quite substantial existing earthing arrangements [2]. In the previous SPRAT article, the first and third IIDMs (unfolded) don't have this problem and can be mounted above any kind of earth, changes in the aerial's feed resistance being accommodated as required by ATU adjustment.

The main advantage of a folded IIDM is that it has more 'resonance modes' [3] in its VSWR spectrum, with better prospects for matching when used on other bands than the design frequency. So if you want to try the folded version without worrying about earthing provision, you can put the spade back in the shed and adopt an easier approach. Here's how.

In Fig. 1, explicit grounding points are now replaced by a bridging wire RS, with the element dimensions differing only slightly from the original. Fig. 2 shows the EZNEC™ predicted VSWR curves for (A) perfect ground and no losses, (B) perfect ground with copper losses, and (C) copper losses and a really poor ground with conductivity = 0.001 siemens/metre and relative permitivity (dielectric constant) of 2. Bare 2mm diameter wire is assumed. Here, both Cm capacitors (Fig. 4) are 48pF.

Table 1 gives wire coordinates and dimensions for a generic (lossless) aerial. In the interests of safety from 'trip wire' hazards, ungrounded IIDM aerials may be raised further above ground with only slight effects on the matching. The experimenter could also mitigate the extra height problem by lowering the X-elevation, without undue detriment to the FF pattern. If in doubt, check (e.g., in EZNEC™) before constructing.

Fig. 3a shows the predicted FF pattern for lossless conditions, for which zenith gain is in excess of 8dBi. The FF pattern for inclusion of copper losses and real ground is shown in Fig. 3b. Lossy grounds are expected to degrade the zenith gain for both dipoles and IIDMs to around 6dBi or less. Matching adjustments for aerials over lossy ground are best done at the aerial end. If a toroidal transformer is used (Fig. 4) then the turns ratio can be adjusted accordingly (turns ratio = square root of antenna resistance ratio).

Another matching approach is to progressively shorten the antenna, while increasing Cm capacitor values, until SWR (for 50 ohms, at the antenna) is close to 1:1 at band centre. For real ground and copper losses, all lengths are reduced by about 10 percent, depending on terrain, plus at least a further 1% when using PVC covered wire.

If you prefer using the TABLE 1 dimensions and an ATU at the shack, do use good quality low loss feeder. Ideally, and certainly for serious use on other bands, most of the matching should be done at aerial end to avoid increased effects of feeder losses (especially on transmitted power) at higher SWRs. Good experimenting!

References:
[1] Telfer, DJ. (2004). *An NVIS aerial for cramped locations*. SPRAT, Journal of the G-QRP Club, Winter Issue 121. [Fig. 2 of the article].

DUNCAN TELFER
G0SIB/G8ATH
SPRAT 124
AUTUMN 2005

[2] Telfer, DJ and Austin, BA (2001). *Novel antenna design for near vertical incidence skywave (NVIS) HF communications*. Proc. 2nd International Conf. on Advanced System Design, Glasgow.

[3] Telfer, DJ and Spencer, JWS (2004). *Properties and performance of a new compact HF aerial design for multi-band operation*. Proc. 4th Int. Conf. on Advanced System Design, University of Glasgow.   [PDF obtainable from www.cims.org.uk/dtelfer.htm Please note changes to web link.]

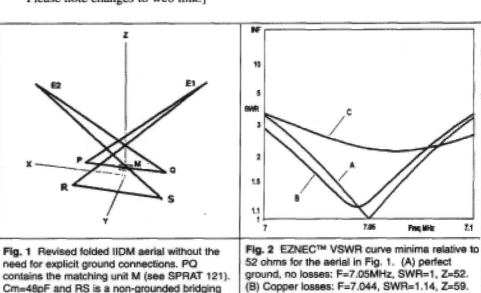

Fig. 1 Revised folded IIDM aerial without the need for explicit ground connections. PQ contains the matching unit M (see SPRAT 121). Cm=48pF and RS is a non-grounded bridging wire. All dimensions are given in TABLE 1.

Fig. 2 EZNEC™ VSWR curve minima relative to 52 ohms for the aerial in Fig. 1. (A) perfect ground, no losses: F=7.05MHz, SWR=1, Z=52. (B) Copper losses: F=7.044, SWR=1.14, Z=59. (C) Real (see text) F=7.062, SWR=2.22, Z=110.

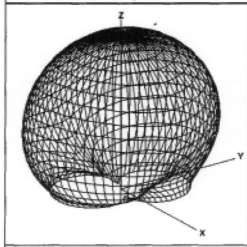

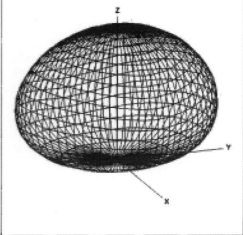

Fig. 3a EZNEC™ FF pattern for aerial of Fig. 1 over perfect ground, no losses (Case A in Fig. 2)

Fig. 3b EZNEC™ FF pattern for aerial of Fig. 1 over real ground and including copper losses (Case C in Fig. 2).

WIRE	DESCRIPTION	END1				END2			Length
		X	Y	Z		X	Y	Z	
1	Element 2	-2600	0	560		5200	2600	9000	11783
4	Element 2	-2600	2600	560		5200	2600	9000	11492
2	Element 1	2600	0	560		-5200	0	9000	11492
5	Element 1	2600	2600	560		-5200	0	9000	11783
3	Matching unit	2600	0	560		-2600	0	560	5200
6	Bridge	-2600	2600	560		2600	2600	560	5200

Wire Table for IIDM antenna of Fig 1.   Units are in mm; wire diameter 2mm.   Cm=48pF

TABLE 1. Dimensions, including wire lengths, for the folded IIDM aerial of Fig. 1. Wire numbering is: 1 E2(Q), 2 E1(P), 3 PQ, 4 E2(S), 5 E1(R), 6(RS). Figures are for the lossless case (A in Fig. 2). The aerial (all Z-values) may be elevated further by up to 2m with little effect on matching and performance. Element X-elevation can be decreased to compensate for this increase in overall height if required (see text).

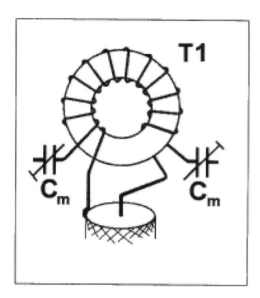

Fig. 4.   (reproduced from SPRAT 121)

The toroidal transformer method of connection between the feeder cable and the pre-match capacitors C_m is quite versatile, allowing the constructor to match antennas of higher or lower resistance than the cable's characteristic impedance, by altering the turns ratio. At this stage an antenna analyser is useful, allowing measurements of the antenna directly (via C_m capacitors) and with T1 in place. Slight adjustments of C_m (together) may also be made, the aim being to achieve SWR (50 ohms) close to 1:1 at the primary winding of T1.

AN 80 AND 40 METRE END-FED ANTENNA

My 21 metre end-wire had given me good service on 40m for a long time, and it was almost invisible. My problem now was to modify it to also work well on 80 metres. Multi-band antennas like the W3DZZ or G5RV were not suitable, because the feeder would have caused an obstruction in my back yard. After a lot of trial and error the problem was solved in the following way. Adding an additional inductor to the existing matching system made it possible to resonate the existing antenna on 80m with an swr of 1.3-1 at 3550 kHz and 1.8-1 at 3500 and 3600 kHz. This was just what I wanted. Fig 1 shows the circuit details. It is mounted in a box made from copperclad material and measuring 7x6x3 inches which is mounted in the roof space adjacent to the point where the antenna wire enters the house. The antenna itself is taken up to the top of a TV mast about 27 feet above ground level, then slopes to the bottom of my back yard. Alignment of the system is simple. Connect a jumper wire between the points XX in Fig 1, then tune the capacitor at the antenna end of L1 for lowest swr on 40m. Then remove the jumper wire and tune the capacitor at the antenna end of L2 for lowest swr on 80m. Repeat the whole process several times to get the best low swr on both bands . Tuning should be carried out at low power, but once tuned 100 watts can be handled. L1 is 25 turns of 1mm diameter enamelled coper wire on a 40mm diameter former and L2 ia is 18 turns of 1.5mm diameter diameter enamelled copper wire on a 30mm diameter former. For best results,especially on 80m, a good earth and/or counterpoise system should be used.

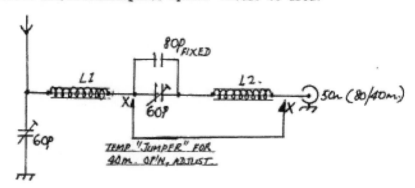

Fig. 1

E VOELLER
DL2QA
SPRAT 111
SUMMER 2002

AN EXPERIMENTAL PRE-TUNED COAXIAL STUB ANTENNA

Assuming that co-axial cable with a velocity factor of 0.66, such as RG58 is used, the length of an antenna can be reduced by approximately one third. The advantage of this is particularly useful at the lower frequencies. For example rather than being 66 feet high a co-axial stub quarter wave antenna for 3.5 MHz will only be approximately 44 feet high, a height much easier to achieve in the average location. Similarly at 28 MHz a stub antenna a quarter wave long is only approximately 5 feet 4 inches long! It has also been found by experiment that such an antenna seems to work quite well on its harmonuc frequencies. For example the model shown in Figure 1 uses a quarter wave stub for 7 MHz, but can be tuned to all frequencies up to 28 MHz. Length for a given band can be calculated by using :-

Length in feet	Length in metres
Quarter wave.	Quarter wave.
234/f x Velocity factor.	71.5/f x velocity factor.
Half wave.	Half wave.
468/f x Velocity factor.	143/f x velocity factor.

f is in meghertz.

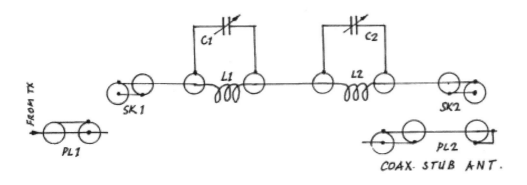

FIGURE 1

Based on previous experience of changing the Cobra into a tuned antenna, it was found that a tuned circuit using a coil made from the shield of the co-ax cable and a suitable variabe capacitor could be used to tune the antenna to all bands between 7 and 28 Mhz. It was then that a sudden idea occurred to the Author.

GUS TAYLOR
G8PG
SPRAT 115
SUMMER 2003

Parallel tuned circuits present a high impedance at resonance, but a low impedance away from resonance, so would it be possible in this particular arrangment to connect two parallel tuned circuits in series and tune them to different bands ? An extra parallel circuit was added, as shown in Figure 1, and the idea worked perfectly, as it did when a third circuit was added temporarily, It is thus possible to use a number of tuned circuits set to different bands and to change bands simply by altering the transmitter output frequency.

Turning now to the details of Figure 1, The lead to PL1 is the co-ax output lead from the transmitter, and is conventionally wired, with the inner carrying the rf and the outer sheath earthed. At SK1 the connections are transposed, with the rf being applied to the outer sheath and the inner conductor being earthed. At L1, three turns of the cable are wound on to a 2 inch (5 cm) diameter former and secured in place with insulation tape. C1 is a 500p variable capacitor. It is connected to the co-axial cable sheath by carefully removing some of the cable outer inulation and using crocodile clips. The circuit L2/C2 is made in exactly the same way. SK2/PL2 allow the rf-carrying outer sheath of the tuner to be connected to the outer sheath of the co-ax stub antenna, the outer sheath and inner conductor being conected together at the far end of the stub. In the experimental model the stub was cut as a quarter wave for 7 MHz (22 feet).

Experiments with this antenna were caried out over a period of weeks, using 3 watts of cw. Despite very poor conditions on the higher bands results have been quite promising. What we need now is further data from different locations, so how about it you antenna enthusiasts ? Another idea at the back of my mind is a pretuned,multi-band counterpoise system using stubs.Please experiment with stubs and report your results.

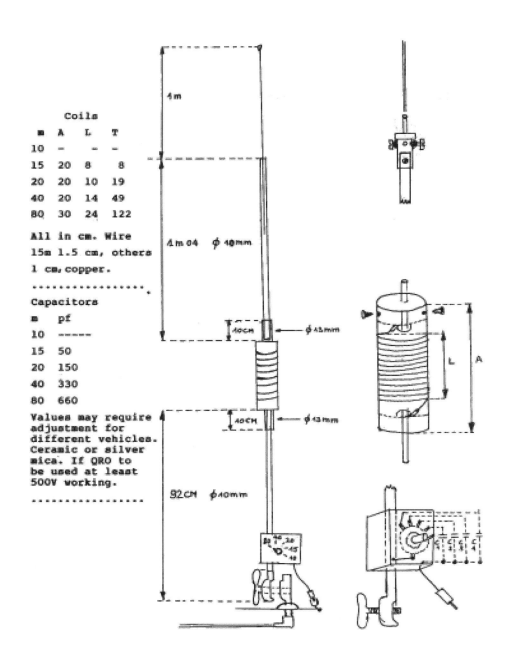

Coils

m	A	L	T
10	-	-	-
15	20	8	8
20	20	10	19
40	20	14	49
80	30	24	122

All in cm. Wire
15m 1.5 cm, others
1 cm, copper.

....

Capacitors

m	pf
10	-----
15	50
20	150
40	330
80	660

Values may require
adjustment for
different vehicles.
Ceramic or silver
mica. If QRO to
be used at least
500V working.

....

G DE SMEDT
ON5NO
SPRAT 105
WINTER 2000/1

The base is a discarded 2 metre antenna base which incorporates a suitable co-axial connector. It is permanently mounted on the vehicle. The lower section of the antenna consists of a 92cm length of 10mm diameter aluminuim tubing. Near its base it has clamped to it the plastic box holding the matching capacitors. The centre section is a 1.04 metre length of 10mm diameter aluminium tubing with the inner part of a PL co-axial connector attached to its top end. This is screwed to the tubing and has three small nuts soldered into its soldering holes. Bolts passing through these nuts secure the top section and allow its effective length to be varied. The top section is the top of an old CB antenna, but a suitaable 1m long telescopic antenna could be used instead. Coil sizes and winding data are given in the Table on the diagram. The ends of each coil former have a 2cm deep wooden plug inserted and held in place by three small woodscrews. A 13mm diameter hole is drilled at the centre of the plugs and a 14 cm length of 13mm diameter aluminium tubing is fixed in this hole with 10 cm protruding. A solder tag is attached to the inner end of the tube by means of a self-tapping screw, and a flexible wire lead from this tag is connected to the associated end of the coil winding. The capacitor box contains a 5-position switch , the capacitors as shown in the Table on the diagram, and an insulated pluglead which connects to a socket on the vehicle body. The plastic box provides weather protection for the switch and capacitors. The coils are weatherproofed by covering the windings with heatshrink tubing and the ends with rubber caps. On 10m the antenna is resonated in the desired part of the band by adjusting the effective length of the top section. On other bands the length of the top section and the value of capacitor in the switch box are varied for resonance at the desired frequency. Note that on other vehicles the value of C required may be different. (The possibility of using a variable capacitor seems well worth investigating .Ed.) Some surprising DX has been worked with the antenna, including three continents on 40 metres.

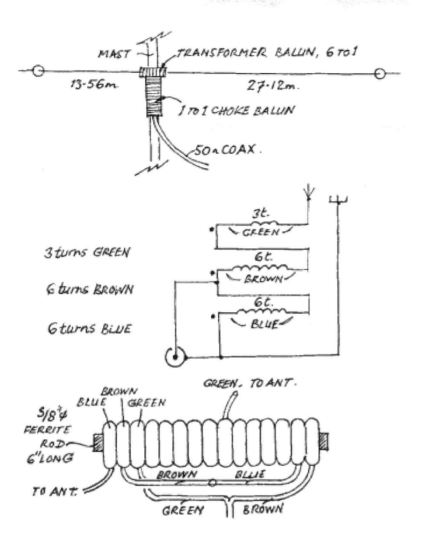

The antenna covers 80m – 10m. SWR is less than 1.4:1 on all bands except 21 MHz (3:1) and 10.1 MHz (5:1).

The transformer balun is wound on a 12 inch long ferrite rod (or two 6 inch rods butted together) and the choke balun has a smaller core. If both horizontal and vertical radiation is desired the choke balun can be omitted. The antenna can also be erected as an inverted V.

It has proved to be a good all band co-ax fed antenna.

**T SORBIE
GM3MXN
SPRAT 105
WINTER 2000/1**

50MHz
REFLECTOMETER/ATU

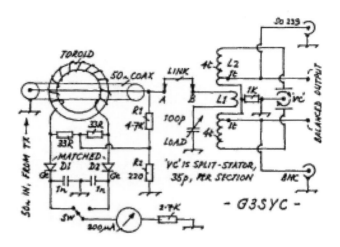

This unit was built for use with an FT690/11 to provide a match facility with
various aerials for /P operation. It has in fact been been used principally
at the home QTH. Besides use with 75ohm twin feeder, provision has been made
to match low Z coax with both PL239 and BNC termination (you never know what
you have to accommodate).
Initally the reflectometer is set up by removing the link AB and connecting a
50ohm dummy load from A to earth. Power is fed in, and with the switch in the
reflected power position. R1/R2 are chosen to give zero reflected power. The
resistor in series with the meter must be chosen to suit the FSD on the
forward power position. this scale can then be calibrated to suit your own
needs. The link is replaced and the dummy load replaced. A 100 pF capacitor
was used for loading but a 50pF capacitor would probably do.
Taps at 1 turn have been used in this unit and has proved satisfactory so
far. However, 300ohm feeder or even open wire can be accommodated by using
tapping points further out from the centre.
The reflectometer and ATU can be built as separate units but a complete unit
is more conveniant to use. A twin meter version can be constructed,
eliminating the switch, and allowing forward and reflected power to be viewed
simultaneously. The unit is easily accommodated in a box 3 x 3 1/2 x 6
inches. If you require more information please contact me.

D1 D2. Germanium diodes matched for forward and reverse resistance.

L2. 8 turns 1inch inside diameter, 16SWG enamelled wire. 1/2 inch gap
in centre for L1.

L1. 2 turn link coil, 16SWG.

TOROID. 13 turns on small ferrite toroid having good HF performance.
(the pototype toroid was of unknown origin).

The 1K resistor from the centre of the coil to earth is to leak away any
static.

BRIAN
G3SYN
SPRAT 54
SPRING 1988

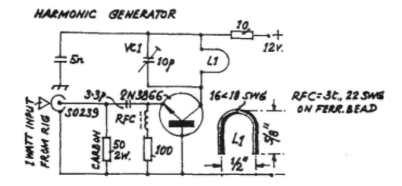

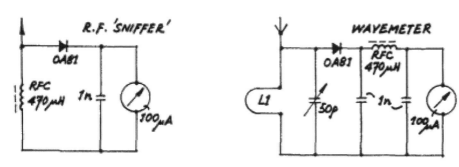

Most newcomers to Amateur radio will, like myself, make straight for the two metre band. To comply with our licence we require a wave-meter that covers 144 - 288MHz or more, 288MHz being the second harmonic. Commercial wave-meters cost about £15 - £20, whereas a home-made one only costs about £3! The difficult part about making a wave-meter is the calibration of the second harmonic point on the dial.

Here is a circuit that can be connected to the output of a 2 metre 'black box', to generate the second harmonic.

R1 is a dummy load and can be 47 or 51 ohms carbon resistor at two watts. RFC is three turns of 22 SWG on a ferrite bead and TR is a 2N3866.

Set-up and Use:-

1. Connect a 12 volt suppy.
2. Connect your rig to the SO.239 and do not put more than 1.5 watts into this circuit.
3. Place a RF sniffer near L1 and key the microphone, adjust VC1 for maximum reading on the RF sniffer.
4. As you can see the RF sniffer can become a wave-meter and use the same components. Do not go to a lot of expense over the above circuits, or you will defeat the object!

Calibration :-

After the harmonic generator and wave-meter have been constructed, calibration can begin. First, check that the wave-meter responds to a 144MHz carrier. If the vanes of the 50pF capacitor are almost fully meshed at this point, all is well, and you should be able to find the second harmonic with the tuning capacitor near minimum (un-meshed).

GEOFF GARDNER
G6MCZ
SPRAT 37
WINTER 1983/4

TWO METRE ATU

DAVID ACKRILL
G0DJA
SPRAT 49
WINTER 1986/7

70MHz DOUBLE TURNSTLE ANTENNA

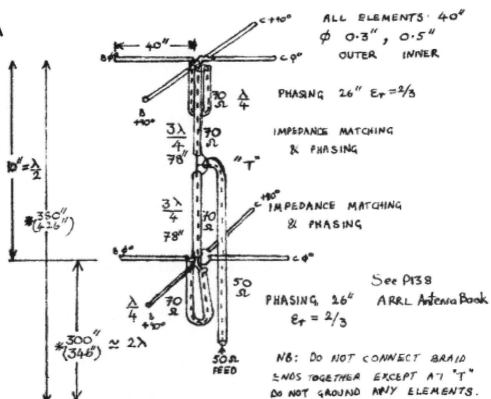

ALL ELEMENTS 40"
φ 0.3", 0.5"
OUTER INNER

PHASING 26" Er = 2/3

IMPEDANCE MATCHING & PHASING

IMPEDANCE MATCHING & PHASING

See P138
ARRL Antenna Book

PHASING 26"
Er = 2/3

NB: DO NOT CONNECT BRAID ENDS TOGETHER EXCEPT AT "T"
DO NOT GROUND ANY ELEMENTS.

JOHN BEECH
G8SEQ
SPRAT 103
SUMMER 2000

I often hear people say "but I haven't got an antenna for 2 metres". There is really no excuse as the rest of this article shows. Dave, G0DJA, won his QRP CW Award using 1 to 3 watts, a bit of wire and this ATU. Best DX GD–land from Birmingham! The ATU is not original; it was described originally by G3UUS in a 1983 Ham Radio Today, and later, briefly, in a note in Technical Topics (RadCom, May 1988, page 350) ascribed to G0DJA and G8NDJ.

Fig. 1 shows the circuit, which consists of a tuneable pi-network low pass filter followed by a half wave length of 50 ohm coax which operates as a phase inverter when balanced output is required. When used with an unbalanced output, the coax forms, of course, simply an extra length of coax in series with the feeder to the antenna.

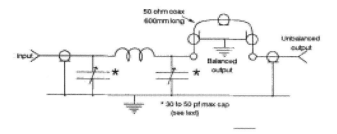

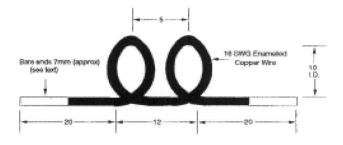

Figure 2 shows details of the coil, and figure 3 a suitable chassis layout. The latter is made, conveniently, from 18 swg aluminium sheet bent into a U-shape. The capacitors may be Jackson type C804 air spaced variables. Those used by the author had short stand-off threaded studs for fixing to the aluminium front panel (see photo) and require the rotators 'earthed' using braid removed from a short length of RG58U or similar coax. Capacitors which have the single threaded screw fixing would be equally suitable. Those used by the author had 7 fixed and 7 moving vanes. The bared ends of the coil wire are wrapped around the adjacent pillars holding the fixed vanes of the two capacitors and soldered. Two s0239 sockets (or other type to suit your equipment) will be required for the unbalanced input and output termination's, plus a couple of 3mm banana plug sockets for the balanced output connections. The phasing line consists of 600mm (measured between connection tails) of RG58U coax or similar 50 ohm cable. Two control knobs are also needed.

JOHN BEECH
G8SEQ
SPRAT 77
WINTER 1993/4

In use, the input to the ATU is connected to the transceiver antenna socket via an SWR meter. In the Author's opinion, the coax between the transceiver output and the SWR meter should never be shorter than half wavelength long, whether or not an ATU is used, particularly on bands above 50 MHz. On 2 metres, therefore, 750mm (26") is recommended (or simple multiples thereof). 12" or so may be neater in many station layouts but can lead to the puzzling condition whereby the SWR meter reads close to 1:1 while the PA stage shuts down refusing to operate with what is, in fact, an SWR greater than 2:1!! Since the conditions at either end of a half wavelength line are the same (all conditions repeat at half wave intervals along the whole length of a feeder) using a half wavelength between transceiver and SWR meter makes adjustment of antenna matching much easier. Connect the antenna feeder(s) to the appropriate output termination of the ATU and, using a repeater or beacon as a test signal, adjust the two capacitors in the ATU in turn to obtain a maximum S-meter reading.

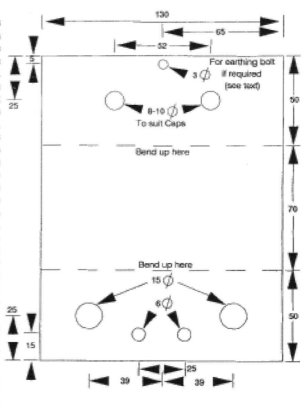

Final adjustment of the capacitors is best made on TX using low power and an unoccupied channel to obtain minimum SWR - and don't forget to give your callsign and say you are testing! You never know, someone may give you a call and you can test your ATU!

2m POCKET ZEPP

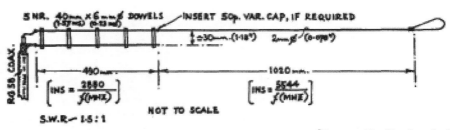

HERBERT HANRIDER
DL7MAM
SPRAT 33
WINTER 1982/3

The elements can either be heavy gauge wire or alloy (1/2 to 1/4 inch diameter). The distance between the radiator and stub is 2 inches or less. Adjustments can be made to the length of the radiator and stub (or distance between the two) for minimum SWR. When fitted to a metal mast the base of the stub can be connected direct with an insulator to take the radiator at this point.

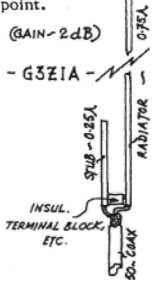

(GAIN ~ 2 dB)

- G3ZIA -

RADIATOR 0.75λ

STUB ~ 0.25λ

INSUL.
TERMINAL BLOCK,
ETC.

50 COAX

D JENNINGS
G3ZIA
SPRAT 41
WINTER 1984/5

2 ELE 2m BEAM

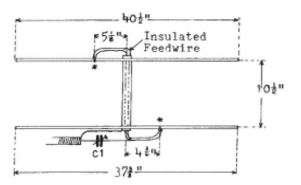

40½"

5⅛" → Insulated Feedwire

1'0½"

C1 ← 4¼" →

37½"

* Bare wire ends fixed with clips - adjust taps for forward gain.
C1 = 3-30pF beehive trimmer adjusted for min. S.W.R.

Original idea by HB9CV, with credits to G3NOW and G3HXQ.

STAN PERCIVAL
G3BGR
SPRAT 12
DECEMBER 1977

BNC-TO-PL259 ADAPTOR

Although experienced VHF/UHF constructors know better most commercial manufacturers still enjoy finishing their VHF/UHF equipment with SO239 aerial sockets requiring "shielded bananaplugs" (PL or "Power Loss" 259) on the end of your cables.

Unfortunately this causes losses up to over 6 dB at 430 MHz as above 50 MHz the impedance of these connectors only approach 50 Ohms within very wide margins. No wonder that those of us who use the higher frequencies for more than a local chat often prefer to use "BNC" connectors. But what to do when suddenly confronted with a commercial radio? One solution is to modify the rig. If this is not possible an adapter comes in handy. Although readily available a BNC to PL259 adapter can be easily built. With parts from local rallies or your own junkbox this is usually a cheaper solution anyway! Use a hot solder iron, preferably 80 Watt or more. Do I hear someone moan about extra losses being introduced by using this adapter? Well, better take it for granted. After all, an adapter is a compromise to adapt commercial errors to appropriate standards.

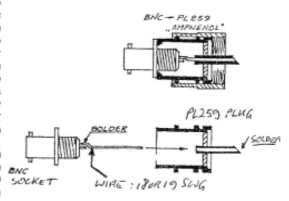

ROBERT VAN DER ZAAL
PA3BHK
SPRAT 84
AUTUMN 1995

VHF/HF POWER METER

R1 and R4 - 300Ω /1W. If you need 50Ω input you should add another two resistors in parallel to R1 and R4. All components are gathered in a small metal box. It could be constructed from PCB. Measurement is made with the base multi-meter with input impedance 30KΩ /V. The output power of the transmitter over 75 Ω load should be calculated as follows:

$$P\ out\ =\ \frac{U^2}{R\ load}$$

or in our case:

$$P\ out\ =\ \frac{U^2}{75}$$

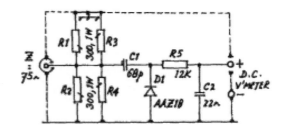

I was very surprised that this simple project was absolutely correct up to 5w output even on 144Mz when compared with commercial watt meter. Powers over 5 watts are dangerous for the load resistor R1 - R4 and D1 - AAZ18. . With 8 watts D1 was destroyed. So I think that for our purposes up to 3w out.)this is an ideal cheap weekend project. If the multimeter has different input impedance than 30kΩ/V then R5 should be calculated as follows; R5=0.414 x z/input impedance of multimeter. R1 - R4, C1 and D1 should be mounted as close as possible to the input socket.

I can send any other information about the wattmeter and also the diode AAZ18 to all interested members.

Now some information for your column. In 1986 during Perseides I made Ms QSOs with IK2DMF on SSB and RB5EF on CW. The power was 3 watts output and ant was a 9 ele F9FT. So QRPers don't worry so much about your small power for Ms. Have a try.

HARRY POPOV
LZ1BB
SPRAT 55
SUMMER 1988

A VHF ABSORPTION WAVEMETER

FIG.1.

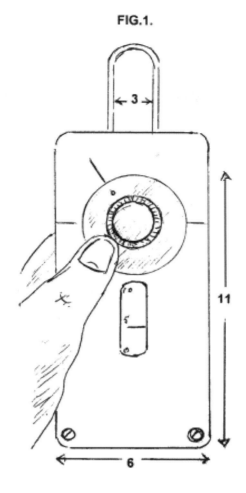

I hold no brief for the originality of the circuitry. The wavemeter fulfils the DTI minimum requirement for frequency measurement. And if calibrated carefully will be accurate enough for most purposes. The coverage of my wavemeter is 120 to 240 MHz approx.

The circuitry is built into the lid of the die cast box, and the frequency range controlled by the LC ratio. The range of interest may therefore be arranged by change of capacity value of coil shape or size. My meter shows the 2 metre band at about 60 °.

The unit is self supporting or may be held in one hand. The case is an 11 x 6 x 3cm die cast box, Fig. 1,2,3. Its size is dependant upon the depth of the meter, in this case the meter, an ex - dip meter is 2 cm deep by 2 cm wide. 1 mA FSD. When drilling the die cast lid, which should be clamped firmly. Mark centre pop and drill three or four smaller holes first, and finish the slot using a router, rotary file or round and half round files. Fit meter and secure with a suitable adhesive/epoxy resin.

HARRY FROGGATT
G3SOX
SPRAT 90
SPRING 1997

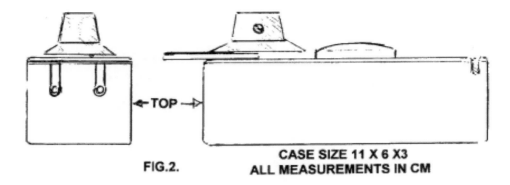

FIG.2.

CASE SIZE 11 X 6 X3
ALL MEASUREMENTS IN CM

VC is a small 50pF capacitor - cut down and left with one or two fixed or moving vanes. The shaft is 6.4 mm dia and takes a small instrument knob 4 cm wide x 2 cm deep. A narrow slot is cut into the near face of the knob, and a small piece of 20 - 24 swg wire is secured to the grooved knob using araldite, to cut out the dial pointer.

The dial is a 6 mm x 4 mm piece of 2 mm Plastic Sheet, covered with white card. Some trimmers are secured with two small setscrews, if the coves, will have to be counter sunk after drilling, and suitable c/s set screws fitted. Other trimmer capacitors have a single nut fixing, in which case the plastic dial will need to be slotted to fit the capacitor spindle and secured by the nut. Some capacitors may require the earth tag to be securely fixed to the ceramic body to prevent slight movement of the tuned circuit during use. Use ARALDITE or some other suitable medium.

Slip the pieces of sleeving on to the coil, after shaping solder D1 to the 320 +/- capacitor and to the coil, Fig.3 about 2 cm from the end.
A small piece of hook up wire is soldered to the end of the coil, disc capacitor and meter. The junction of D1 and disc capacitor is soldered to the other side of the meter. D1 is a LN4148, any small signal diode should work okay. Slots are filed in the top of the case to facilitate removal of the lid and change of coils.

Calibration is "off air", using a friends 2 metre TX, or by dip meter signal generator.

A two turn coil, and a capacitor with 2 fixed & 2 moving vanes will enable operation into the lower VHF region. 6 metres - 10 metres. The dial will not be exactly linear.

All the bits plus case were found in my "junk box."

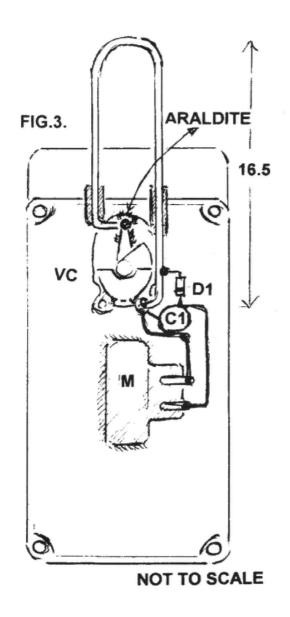

FIG.3.

ARALDITE

16.5

VC

D1

C1

M

NOT TO SCALE

A TWO ELEMENT 50MHz BEAM

For the past three years, the consuming amateur radio interest has been 50 MHz. As the 50 MHz equipment centered about a Yaesu FT690/2 some portable operation seemed natural. However on the occasions when such activity was undertaken the antenna system used was a dipole. Whilst useful contacts resulted antenna limitations and indifferent conditions did not give especially memorable experiences. This spring renewed interest in /P required that a better system be provided.

The following needs were to be satisfied:

1. Useful gain.
2. Reasonable back to front ratio.
3. Good matching to 50 ohm coaxial feeder.

4. Easy to erect etc. and robust.

The resulting two element parasitic beam is considered to meet the above requirements rather well. Its performance literally in the field has been pleasing.

Construction was based on generally easily available plastic dipole centres and aluminium tubing procured from the usual sources. The diagrams with this text are intended to be more or less self explanatory and where necessary further comment is provided. Plumber's delight construction is avoided by the already mentioned plastic dipole centres for both the driven element and the reflector to suit item four above and in the authors case, patently better performance.

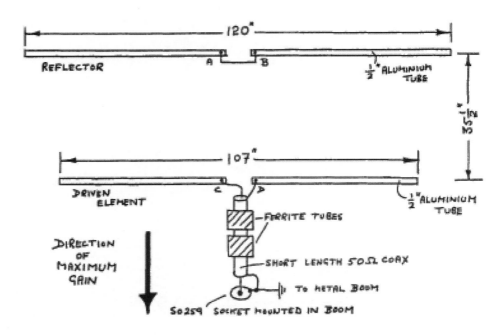

BRIAN BOOTH
G3SYC
SPRAT 64
AUTUMN 1990

AB and CD represent the gaps in the centre of each element (1.5 inch) due to the insulators. In the case of AB this is bridged by a piece of brass strip, CD being connected to a short piece of 50 ohm coax. This latter item being threaded through ferrite tubes to form a sleeve balun. The other end of the coax being terminated at a SO239 socket mounted in the metal boom (1 inch square tube) near the driven element. The ferrite tubes were of unknown origin but they had been used for the same function on some salvaged UHF cables. The holes through the tubes were such that the "stripped" braid just fitted comfortably.

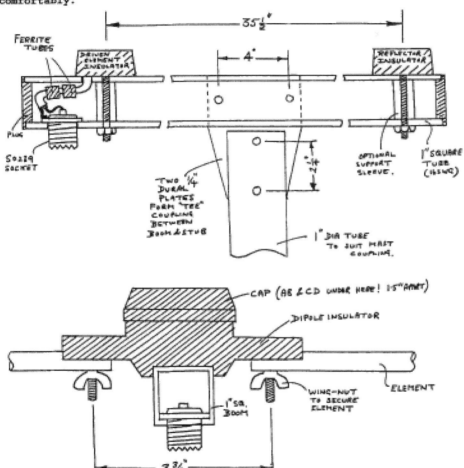

The boom was connected to its mast with the aid of a short tubular section using two dural plates and suitable bolts. The removal of one bolt allows the tubular section to be folded along the boom helping storage. The reader will have to devise a suitable transition to the mast to be used.

Wing nuts provide easy assembly/knock down features. When folded with elements left on the insulators the overall length measured 75 inches. Aluminium plugs were provided at the inboard end of each element to prevent crushing upon tightening the wing nuts, the plugs being secured by a smear of Araldite adhesive.

An initial test with G3KNU showed an excellent match to the feeder plus a substantial back to front ratio. The physical removal of the reflector leaving it as a dipole only, indicated a very respectable gain for the beam.

Further field experience with this beam and powers from 0.25 to 10 watts has been interesting and quite rewarding. Many European countries have been very easy to work at excellent signal strengths. A sceptical G4HBA was persuaded to take a second version of this antenna to his new QTH in Devon to provide some continuity to his 6m. activity. With this beam at low height, one of his first contacts was with Z23JO.

In conclusion it would appear that quite a useful portable beam has resulted. The original aims have been very substantially realised not the least being portability and robustness. This beam is worthy of consideration by intending /P operators.

THREE ELEMENT HB9CV BEAM

In the VHF Section of SPRAT 29, David, G4DHF reproduced a design for a three-element beam from G8PON.

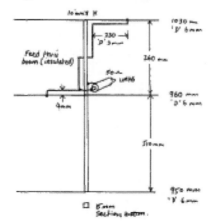

This is a modification of the popular HB9CV 2m two-element portable antenna.
David concludes that "this handy little antenna will provide a useful 6dB+ gain."

AJ MORGAN
G8PON
SPRAT 29
WINTER 1981/2

A FIVE ELEMENT QUAD FOR TWO METRES

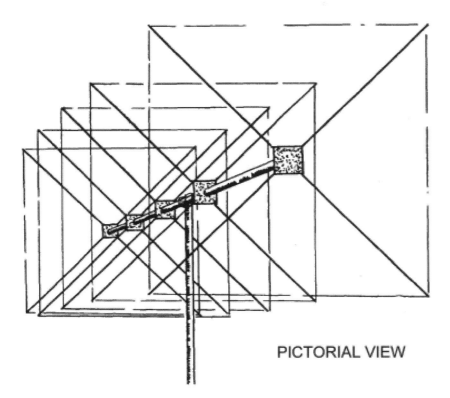

PICTORIAL VIEW

The S5Q works well for me, I hope it will do the same for any of the members who have a mind to build it. Standing beside me in the workshop this antenna will open the Dover repeater (approximately 70 miles) on one watt. I have also worked a contact in The Hague with the antenna in the workshop, so great things are expected when I get it out in free space this week-end. All the antennas I develop have the guy with little space and few bundles of QRX around, in mind, so the S5Q is simple to build, small and cheap.

WHAT YOU WILL NEED TO BUILD THIS FANTASTIC ANTENNA!

5 x wood blocks, 2¾ x 2¾ x ⅝ inches.
1 x 4 feet length of 1 inch dowel, or a broom handle.
6 x 4 feet lengths of ¼ inch dowel.
26SWG enamelled copper wire.

1 strip of connector blocks.
PVC tape.
Glue and screws.
Tin of out door varnish.
Press tacks to set wires in position

Cover the boom with PVC tape, remembering the ends, apply two coats of varnish and leave to dry well. The wood blocks should have the corners squared off so that there is a flat area to drill. Mark off the centre of the block and drill a one inch hole, or to suit the boom. Drill a ¼ inch hole at each corner down into the centre hole. With the wood block flat, measure down ¼ inch from each corner to the centre and drill a 1/16 inch hole right through the block. These holes are to hold the arms in place. On one side of each block drill a ⅛ inch hole to the centre hole. These holes take the screws that hold the blocks to the boom. Two coats of varnish.

To obtain the spacing measure and mark the boom from one end, which will be the placing of the reflector. 16 - 13 - 8 - 8 inches. The space between the reflector and the driven element will thus be 16 inches and between the driven element and the first director 13 inches, and between the directors, 8 inches.

JOHN STEVENSON
G8ZRY
SPRAT 32
AUTUMN 1982

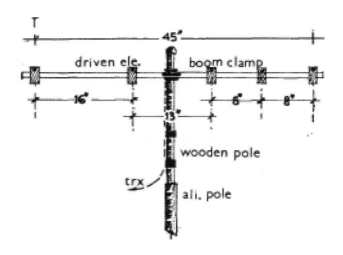

The length of the wire is 87 inches for the reflector, 77 for the directors and 83 for the driven element. To make the spider arms, cut the ¼ inch dowel into 20 x 16 inch lengths, cover with PVC tape and varnish twice and allow to dry well. The antenna should be fed with 50 ohm coax, which should be taped down the element arm to the connector block. The SWR is flat, not above 1.4:1.

Use press pins to set the wires in position on the arms, each side is approximately equal. Drill a small hole through the arms at those points and thread the wire through, remove the centre metal parts from the single connector blocks so that both screws hold the wire, and varnish the metal contact. When the elements are all mounted on the boom, pull arms lightly to make the wire taut, drill through the arms via 1/16 inch holes in the wood block, cover a match stick with wood glue and press through. When dry this will hold the arms solid. Screw wood blocks to the boom via ¼ inch.

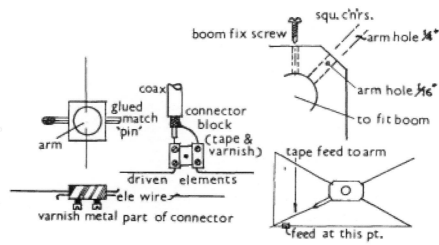

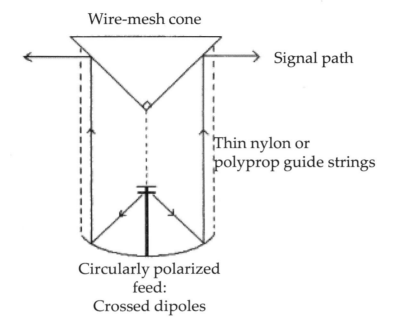

Wire-mesh cone

Signal path

Thin nylon or
polyprop guide strings

Circularly polarized
feed:
Crossed dipoles

A high-gain omni-directional antenna for 23cm and above

The dish and feed produce a circularly polarized beam) direction
NOT important)
This is intercepted by the cone, which has a solid right-angle at its
point. The result is a horizontally polarized omni-directional
signal.
The cone should be a slightly larger diameter than the dish and
can be suspended at any convenient height above the dish,
provided tahe dish and cone are levelled, otherwise the beam tilts.
The maximum theoretical gain is the dish gain -3bB because of the
circular polarization, less a few dB in practice for under
illumination of the cone.

**JOHN BEECH
G8SEQ
SPRAT 121
WINTER 2004/5**

This antenna is based on an existing dish design and the experiments were all done at 23 cm and 600 nm. If you already have a dish antenna, the only mods you need to do are: 1) replace the feed with a circularly polarized feed, 2) alter the mount so the dish points vertically upwards, 3) build & suspend a cone above the dish.

The antenna is actually a FLYSWATTER, but the trapezoidal reflector is replaced with a cone with a 90 deg. Included angle. In section this gives a continuous reflecting face at 45 deg. to the vertically radiated signal, which causes this to be radiated in all directions as a horizontal signal. In order to illuminate the cone evenly, the dish must produce a circularly polarized signal. The overall result is a horizontally polarized omni-directional signal. Anyone who is not convinced, try this simple experiment. Take a standard LED and file the lens end flat. Now drill the end of the LED (ie. the face you have just filed) with a drilled ground at 90 deg.. Connect the LED to a suitable power source and hold it upright in a darkened room. You will see a horizontal line on all the walls in the room. If you can't darken the room, make a paper cylinder about 15 cm diameter to place around the LED.

The remarkable thing about this design of antenna is that you (theoretically) only loose 3dB gain from what the dish would have given had it been pointed directly at the station you want to work. In practice the losses are slightly greater due to under illumination of the cone. This can be minimized by making the cone slightly larger than the dish diameter and not mounting it too high above the dish. The height of the cone should be chosen such that the out going and incoming signals clear any nearby objects such as trees buildings or parked cars.

This antenna was first tested on VHF NFD last year. Only a few stations were worked due to lack of man-power (we weren't entered on the band), but we were able to compare received signal strengths with distant stations as we retained the ability to point the dish directly at the station, a manoeuvre which only took 30 seconds. This confirmed that the omni was less than an S-point down on the directly pointed dish. We had in fact left the dish mounted on the roof rack of our vehicle and suspended the cone from a counterbalanced gibbet about 6m above the ground. The height between the feed point to the dish and the tip of the cone was about 1.5m.